MOTIVATION: *A Biological Perspective*

STUDIES IN
Psychology

Consulting Editor:

L. JOSEPH STONE

Vassar College

MOTIVATION
A Biological Perspective

John L. Fuller

Roscoe B. Jackson Memorial Laboratory

RANDOM HOUSE · NEW YORK

Fourth Printing, November 1966

© *Copyright, 1962, by Random House, Inc.*

Library of Congress Catalog Card Number: 62-19367

Manufactured in the United States of America
by The Colonial Press Inc.

Contents

MOTIVATION: *A Biological Perspective*

[I]

Introduction

IN TRYING TO understand the behavior of another person we always seek to discover his motives, and the goals for which he strives. If we sit in judgment upon his acts, our opinion is tempered by an interpretation of his motivation. Our response to his boastful assertion, "I'm a better man than you," is dependent upon whether we consider it to be motivated by an underlying feeling of inferiority, by a sense of superior social position, or simply by a robust sense of humor.

To control the behavior of others we try to provide motivation. The coach gives fight talks to his team, parents reward children for good behavior with candy or words of praise, teachers give high grades as rewards for study. The profession of advertising is based upon the attempts of sellers to motivate other people to buy their goods.

Such aspects of motivation seem at first thought to be far removed from biology, and to belong exclusively to the field of psychology. But further consideration will bring out at least two ways in which our biological nature influences motivational structure. First, man never outgrows his physiological needs, nor the behavior patterns which satisfy them. Hunger, sexual desire, and pain are powerful motives even in the most sophisticated human life. Second, such human motives as scientific curiosity, the urge for power, for money, for personal recognition appear as the child develops mentally and physically. The problems of great import to psychology are the extent to which these motives are expressions of primary biological needs, and the extent to which the motives of the adult are modified by the satisfaction or frustration of biological needs in youth. The purpose of this study is to range over the area of motivation and to integrate the contributions of biology and psychology to its problems.

MOTIVES, DRIVES, AND NEEDS

To *motivate* someone is to impart motion to him, in other words, to produce a *response*. The basic meaning of motivation is shown by its roots in the Latin *movere,* to move. Regarded objectively, motivation may appear to be very much the same thing as stimulation, a word derived from the Latin *stimulus,* a goad or a whip. If living organisms always responded in exactly the same manner to a stimulus (the word is now being employed in the ordinary English sense) there would indeed be no reason for bringing in the concept of motivation. However, common experience teaches that there is much variation in responses to similar stimuli. Seeing and smelling steak and onions arouses different responses in us, depending upon when we last ate. We sit up late to finish an exciting novel but drowse over a history assignment, although both tasks involve similar motor activity guided by similar physical stimuli. To explain the fact that a stimulus does not invariably elicit the same response, psychologists use hypothetical model systems composed of intervening variables. One of these is the concept of *drive:* a measure of the strength of the tendency of the organism to respond to specific types of stimuli, or as some would prefer to say, a measure of the tendency to go toward a goal.

A term such as drive may be considered as an abstraction which need not be physically defined provided it is useful in predicting behavior. Alternatively, one may devote much effort to the attempt to define drive strength in terms of physiological state. Many psychologists tacitly accept a physiological theory of drive, though they are willing to leave the research in this area to biologists. One concept which has widely influenced theories of motivation is that a drive is a function of the internal state of an organism related to its primary biological needs. Thus we require particular kinds of nutrients which can be oxidized in our tissues to provide energy for keeping alive. Immediately after eating, these needs are satisfied and the hunger drive is at a low level. As the food is used up in metabolism, drive level gradually increases, and there is increased activity and responsiveness to stimuli associated with eating.

We can draw up lists of needs which will be longer or shorter depending upon how specifically we catalogue them. There is not a single requirement for food, for example, but we could list needs for perhaps thirty or forty different kinds of nutrients, some required in minute quantity only. It is a truism that for survival, behavior must be geared to all these innate needs, but it is also true that the physiology of each need is somewhat specific. The consequences of deprivation of an essential substance may affect the organism within seconds, minutes, hours, or even months. Such differences in time scale generate important psychological differences. The distribution in space of the objects necessary to satisfy biological needs is another factor to be considered. Air is all about us to provide oxygen, but food must be sought, sex partners must be courted. The need for sleep is best satisfied by the avoidance of external stimulation.

One argument of this paper will be that the physiological diversity of these needs entails a corresponding diversity of psychological consequences. Theories which employ a particular type of drive in a particular species as a model for all motivation are likely to be limited in their application. Yet learning theorists have generalized widely from experiments on rats motivated by hunger, thirst, or pain, while Freud attempted to explain human motivation in terms of libido derived from sexual drives. It is not surprising that the two systems do not fit together very well.

Drives have sometimes been classified as biogenic or psychogenic, the former associated with physiological processes and the latter with the organism's perception of its environment. Another dichotomy recognizes primary or innate, and secondary or acquired drives. In a general way the biogenic drives are considered to be innate, and the psychogenic drives to be acquired, but this relationship is not precise. It is possible to acquire an addiction for drugs which has a definite physiological basis, and is in a sense biogenic, though it can scarcely be termed innate. On the other hand, some psychologists and biologists believe that there exist in animals various social, manipulative, and exploratory drives which are innate, but which cannot at present be related to any physiological condition. Only indirectly, if at all, can many aspects of behavior be related to stimuli arising from tissue needs within the organism.

The difficulties of classification are well exemplified by the sex drive. This is certainly dependent partly upon biological factors, but (particularly in humans) it is also a function of individual experience. Individuals have no "need" for sexual functioning in the sense that they have a need for water. Sexual activity in some species, for example the salmon, is actually adverse to the survival of the individual. The point is that one cannot impose an arbitrary classification upon the varieties of motives, and find a neat pigeonhole for each one. Motives vary in the extent to which they are related to tissue need, to internal sensitizing agents such as hormones, to perception of the external world, and to individual experience. Each is more or less unique in these respects.

[II]

Biological Needs and Their Psychological Consequences

EVERY ORGANISM requires certain substances and conditions in its environment for survival. The metabolic needs (food, water, oxygen, and the elimination of waste products) are concerned with the continuous flow of energy through the organism. The integrative needs deal with repair and avoidance of damage to body cells, and include the need for sleep. Finally, reproductive needs are concerned with racial perpetuation rather than individual survival. For man, and for many other species, these include not only provisions for fertilization of an egg cell by a sperm, but arrangements for nurture of the young after birth. This is usually the mother's role, but the male parent may participate. Only man and a few other primates permit individuals other than the biological parents to share the responsibilities of infant care.

To say that men or rats behave as they do in order to satisfy needs is not a scientific explanation of behavior. Nevertheless, it is obvious that survival depends upon the adaptation of behavior to essential needs. The biologist sees two ways in which this might be done. One method involves the development of essential reflexes and instincts. The organism is innately equipped with suitable responses to stimuli in such a way that its needs are fulfilled. The adaptive consequences of these modes of behavior are the result of evolution. Any mutation (change in heredity) which renders its possessor more likely to survive and produce offspring has a better chance of being passed on to descendants than does the original genetic factor. Mutations leading to maladaptive behavior are less likely to be preserved. Over the course of the two billion years that living organisms have occupied the earth this process, which we call *natural selection,* has resulted in the production of thousands of different species, each equipped with behavior adapted to its needs. The variety of adaptations is tremendous and has been well catalogued by naturalists. An animal may be adapted to utilize specialized food plants or to capture prey by force, by lures, or by constructing traps. Many species have elaborate courtship patterns which serve to insure proper timing of the reproductive processes in the two sexes so that fertilization is more likely: for example, the mating dances of grouse and peacocks. Although the details of instinctive behavior are modifiable by experience within limits, it is still true that the adaptive nature of such behavior is traceable to a set of coded instructions in the genes and changes in the instructions can occur only as a result of the slow evolutionary process.

Contrasted with specific adaptations which characterize a whole species as resultants of normal growth is the ability to modify behavior in accordance with experience. This function, which we call learning, reaches its culmination in man. If modification of behavior by learning is to be adaptive it must somehow be regulated by its effect on biological needs. There must be some feedback which insures that satisfying a need will strengthen the behavior responsible for the need reduction. Somehow motives and drives must be attached to needs. This association is the central part of the reinforcement learning theories, whose central theorem may thus be expressed: when an organism responds to a stimulus in such a manner that a drive is reduced, the probability of the same response to that stimulus is thereby increased.

The two modes of adaptation are not mutually exclusive. Some adjustive variation is apparent in the most stereotyped behavior. Likewise, the capacity to modify behavior has a genetic basis, and is not independent of evolution through natural selection. Men and animals can acquire only those responses which are biologically possible for each species.

THE NEED FOR OXYGEN

If the cells of the brain are deprived of oxygen for over two minutes they undergo irreversible damage. Other tissues are less sensitive, but their survival time is still measured in minutes. Because the effects of oxygen deprivation are so severe, and because the adjustment of breathing rate is primarily a matter of reflex response to changes in blood chemistry, there has been little psychological interest in oxygen drive. An asphyxiated rat would have little time to learn a maze with oxygen as the reward, and the very fact of oxygen deprivation would interfere with the learning process. Thus, responses to oxygen lack have been the concern of the physiologist and physician rather than the psychologist. However, every individual has at some time been temporarily stifled by bed clothing, or in a crowd, or under water. Such experiences may produce a strong conditioned response based upon fear of suffocation, and may have important consequences for neurotic behavior.

THE NEED FOR WATER

About four-fifths of our body weight is water. Daily we lose one to two quarts through the kidneys, bowels, skin, and lungs. Total water deprivation may be endured for a period of days, depending upon temperature, humidity, and activity. Many animals drink mostly at night, since this is the time they can most safely approach their sources of water, and this rhythm carries over to laboratory animals who live in cages with water always available. Humans tolerate a considerable variety of drinking schedules, some taking most of their water with meals, while others spread their intake over their waking hours. The amount of liquid taken is partly a matter of habit and opportunity to drink. In spite of variations in intake, the water content of the body is held constant by differential absorption of water in the kidneys resulting in diluted or concentrated urine.

Drying of the mucous membranes of the mouth and pharynx is the local stimulus of thirst. Nerve endings in the dehydrated membranes are stimulated, and impulses reaching the brain mediate both the drive and the conscious experience of thirst. Seeking water and drinking it moistens the pharyngeal membranes, reduces the need, and according to reinforcement theory will become a habitual mode of response. Local drying of the membranes may not necessarily be the consequence of actual deprivation of water. Highly seasoned foods or nervousness may induce a thirst which is just as real as one based upon reduced stores of water in the body.

Control of drinking behavior through direct physical action upon the central nervous system has been demonstrated by Andersson (1953). Goats receiving minute injections of hypertonic sodium chloride solution into the hypothalamus drank large quantities of water; injection of isotonic saline solution had no such effect. Under ordinary conditions such a system provides a behavioral means of controlling the osmotic pressure of body fluids. Increased osmotic pressure leads to injection of water which in turn reduces osmotic pressure. Such systems which maintain some substance or process at a constant level are called *homeostatic*. Much behavior does tend to maintain homeostasis, but it is an oversimplification to elevate this fact to the status of a law of behavior. Falk (1961) has performed ingenious experiments in which animals are stimulated to drink under conditions in which water ingestion is nonhomeostatic.

Under usual circumstances stimuli arising from peripheral structures and physico-chemical influences acting directly upon neurones in the central nervous system set in motion behavior which maintains constant osmotic pressure. Such dual control permits rather accurate regulation, and this precision gave rise to the concept of homeostasis. The idea is useful in behavior as well as physiology, provided it is regarded as a descriptive rather than an explanatory term.

Local stimuli are not the only source of the thirst drive. Rats have been prepared with esophageal fistulae so that water drunk in the normal fashion spills out on the ground after passing over the pharyngeal membranes. Moistening these membranes without actually satisfying the body needs gives only temporary reduction of thirst drive as measured by the amount of drinking. Injecting water through the lower portion of the fistula directly into the stomach reduces the amount of drinking, after time is allowed for absorption of the water into the blood, although the pharynx continues to be dry.

Although the physiological basis of the thirst drive is the need for water, we may learn to slake our thirst by milk, tea, coffee, soft drinks, or beer. These specific thirsts are examples of *appetites*, a term which will be encountered over and over again as we discuss motivation related to hunger, to sex, and even to preferred modes of recreation. The choice of one beverage over another (and a similar principle applies to choice of food, lover, favorite painter or composer) depends upon something other than its ability to satisfy the biological need for water. The something else may be a flavoring extract, a stimulant such as caffeine, or a narcotic such as alcohol. Some beverages have prestige value. Beer drinking in our society is a symbol of adulthood, and young men usually try to like it even though it hurts. It is important to consider whether such habits may actually be inconsistent with biological needs. The stimulating, tasteful, and prestige beverages are mostly water with a small amount of dissolved or suspended material. There is no danger that an appetite for a particular beverage will result in water deficiency, but the additions may be harmful. Soft drinks, milk, or coffee (with cream and sugar) contain calories which may not be needed. Excessive ingestion of alcohol or caffeine can be injurious. There seems to be no built-in homeostatic device which controls the intake of these additives in the way that water intake is regulated by body needs. Hitching an appetite to a primary drive may enrich living, but at the same time it brings risks.

THE NEED FOR FOOD

There is not one need for food, but numerous requirements for specific substances. Nutritionists have found that the essential nutrients for human beings (and needs are similar for other mammals) are about a dozen amino acids (found in proteins), a carbohydrate (sugar or starch), certain forms of fat, a dozen or more vitamins, and about the same number of inorganic salts. Quantitatively, the daily requirements for each type of nutrient vary from a millionth of an ounce up to a pound or so. Today's cookbooks contain sections on the nutritive value of foods, although people fed themselves for thousands of years before there were nutritionists, and most of the world still eats without benefit of these scientists.

The reason that we do not have to be biological chemists in order to eat satisfactorily is that most foods contain many nutrients, and the organism is adapted to wide variations in the quantity of most of these. Animals in their natural habitat generally eat a variety of foods, and any deficiencies are likely to be in overall quantity rather than in specific substances.

When we talk about hunger drive, however, we are generally concerned with the organism's need for energy foods: carbohydrates, fats, and proteins which can be oxidized in the tissues. Sugar is the major fuel of the body, and is the key substance in an elaborate system of hormones and nervous mechanisms which regulate its storage (in an inactive form, glycogen) in liver and muscles from which it is released as needed and carried by the blood to active tissues. Sugar concentration in the blood is believed to be part of the hunger-regulating system.

The onset of hunger is accompanied by strong contractions of the stomach producing what we call "hunger pangs." The intensity of hunger as determined both subjectively and objectively increases with the degree of food deprivation up to a certain point. During prolonged starvation, hunger drive is reported to decrease in both man and animals. Motivation to eat is also influenced by physical and chemical properties of foodstuffs, and most importantly by the habits and attitudes of the organism regarding specific foods.

As in the case of thirst, local factors are insufficient to explain all the facts of eating behavior. Food diluted with a nonnutrient filler stops stomach contractions, but only temporarily abolishes eating. Animals and men can regulate their food intake adequately after surgical removal of the stomach. Recently the importance of the hypothalamus for control of eating has been stressed. Many investigators have shown that bilateral lesions of the ventro-medial nucleus near the midline of the hypothalamus result in enormously increased food intake. Given these lesions, rats, monkeys, dogs, and cats become very obese. In sharp contrast, lesions made a millimeter or two farther to the side in the same region of the brain abolish eating, and a rat with such a lesion will starve to death while surrounded by food. There are rare instances of similar conditions in man where the lesion is a secondary result of a brain tumor. The hypothalamus seems to be a "drive center," containing inhibitory and excitatory centers for eating which are normally in balance. Destroying the inhibitory center results in an obese animal; destroying the excitatory center, in an animal which starves in the midst of plenty. The biological and psychological factors affecting eating converge in this structure.

Recently it has been suggested that the hypothalamic center is directly affected by the blood sugar concentration and that hunger is ordinarily a response to low sugar concentration. The fact that in some conditions (for example in sugar diabetes) an excessive appetite is associated with *high* blood sugar is explained in terms of the impaired ability of the diabetic to utilize sugar. The hypothalamus does not respond to the sugar level directly, but rather to utilizable sugar. The central nervous system thus is affected by the nature of the fluid bathing its cells, by nerve impulses arising from the stomach, and by nerve impulses arising from stimulation by external events. Learning plays a part too, particularly in evaluating the external stimuli, because hunger, much more than thirst, becomes overlaid by habits and appetites which may be deleterious to health. Thus, the development of specific eating habits is of considerable psychological and medical interest.

One of the psychological approaches to this problem is to separate the nutritive consequences from the sensory consequences of eating behavior, and to control the experiential factor by training. A considerable amount of effort and ingenuity has gone into this problem. Two major possibilities have been considered. The first is that the reward value of eating is based upon nutritive values, and that reinforcement occurs when the tissue need is satisfied. Against this idea is the fact that considerable delay intervenes between eating and the utilization of the food, and that psychological association between two events so far apart in time is unlikely. Therefore, say the critics, reinforcement is actually a matter of stimuli associated with the consummatory act of eating, such as the taste, texture, odor, and appearance of the food. At present it looks as though both views were probably right. Animals learn mazes when rewarded by saccharin which tastes sweet, but has no nutritive value. The reinforcement must be dependent upon sensory properties rather than upon the ability to satisfy a need. On the other hand, Chambers (1954) has shown that rabbits can learn to stand on a platform which controls a valve in a system which gives them intravenous injections of the nutritive sugar glucose, but they do not learn when the "reward" is the nonnutritive sugar xylose. Here it seems as though tissue need reduction without the usual sensory correlates of consummatory behavior were sufficient for learning. Some of this work is very recent and must be confirmed by addi-

tional research, but it is not surprising that both types
of reinforcement are effective alone. Actually, in nature they would generally be associated. The question
still remains as to whether the sensory properties of
the food are naturally rewarding, or whether they acquire rewarding properties as a result of reinforcement
by tissue need reduction. This is not an easy problem,
since there is no way to rear an animal without feeding it. Thus its adult taste preferences are always complicated by the fact that the taste of food has been
associated with meeting energy requirements. There
is considerable evidence that many food preferences
which one might consider innate are actually acquired
through training. Dogs which have never been fed
meat will often refuse to eat the finest raw hamburger.
There appears to be no inborn recognition of it as a
food. However, I have noted that it is very easy to
teach a dog to take meat, and the learning takes place
so rapidly that tissue need reduction cannot be responsible. It is possible that in the higher animals
learning is involved in the development of all appetites based upon the nonnutritive qualities of food,
but that organisms are so constructed that learning
occurs more readily with some stimuli than with
others. How well newborn babies discriminate tastes
is uncertain, but they tend to reject bitter and sour
substances more than sweet substances. It is generally
easier to teach children to like candy than to like
olives, but this does not mean that reinforcement
value of sweet taste is innate. I know of one family
in which the children were never given candy as
a reward, nor were they forbidden it. In the absence of any strong social pressures one way or the

other, these children prefer almost any other food to candy. The heavy American consumption of sweets may be attributable to our indoctrination of children with the idea that candy is a symbol of good behavior.

There has been interest in the possibility of separate hungers for specific nutrients based upon body needs rather than taste and odor or habits. Experiments by Harris, Richter, and others demonstrate that such appetites, which are biologically adaptive, do exist. Rats deprived of B vitamins learned to select foods which were rich in these substances. Similarly, rats deprived of their adrenal glands lost salt very rapidly and learned to drink salt water in preference to pure water. The preference was reversed when the adrenal hormones were replaced. In these cases, the effect of the nutrient is so rapid that the principles of reinforcement can operate. One would not expect, nor does one find such favorable results with a nutrient which benefits the animal only after a protracted delay.

There have been a number of studies on the self-regulation of diet in animals. A "cafeteria" system of feeding is used in which the animal has access to purified sources of each nutrient and can select variable proportions of each. Domesticated rats grew well on such a regime, but wild rats were found to make poor choices. Davis showed that children allowed free choice of a variety of nutritious foods often made choices which were bizarre from an adult point of view, but which were adequate as judged by the children's health and rate of growth. These results indicate that human beings may have a certain "wisdom of the body," provided someone who knows nutrition

provides an adequate menu from which suitable biological choices can be made. It does not follow that
appetite is a reliable guide to nutrition when the
opportunity to select is less good, and when the addition of flavors, colors, and changes in the style of the
preparation may prove to be dubious cues to vitamin
and mineral content. Some of the handsomest fruits
and vegetables are least valuable in the diet. Whatever
self-regulatory ability man may have is certainly
swamped by an accumulation of dietary habits acquired during childhood and adolescence. Nutritional
deficiencies are prevalent among economically privi-
leged people who are uneducated in regard to food
values. In historical fact, economic improvement has
led to overconsumption of costly, but biologically
worthless foods, and been on occasions actually detri-
mental to health. There is nothing magical about the
ability of an animal to select a good diet. If malnutri-
tion results in discomfort, an animal may learn to eat
substances which reduce the discomfort. If there are
immediate rewards of flavor associated with biologically unsuitable foods, these may be preferred to more
adequate foods. Secondary rewards for human eaters
are so prevalent that appetites are not likely to be
reliable guides for good nutrition.

Medical science is much concerned with disorders
of the motivations centered about eating, disorders
which may result in allergies, obesity, and malnutri-
tion in the midst of plenty. A final point from animal
experimentation bears on the general problem of
measuring the strength of hunger drive. Offhand one
would say that an animal which eats heavily is one
with a strong drive and would assume that an obese

rat with its hypothalamic lesions, or a genetically obese mouse, becomes fat because it has a stronger drive than an intact rat or a normal mouse. In an ordinary cage with abundant food the obese animals do eat more than normals, but when forced to work for what they get they eat less. Obese animals cut down their intake when food is made bitter by adding quinine; normal animals do this also, but after a few days raise their intake to the usual level. Regulation of food intake in obese animals is predominantly based upon sensory attributes of available food; in normal rats and mice an additional feedback mechanism regulates consumption in accordance with caloric needs.

This particular example focuses our attention upon certain problems of the drive concept. If amount of response is not a reliable indicator of drive strength, what shall we substitute? Should we dispense with the term altogether, since methods of measurement do not agree? These are important questions, and we shall devote a later section to the general problem of quantifying the concepts of drive and motivation.

THE NEED FOR ELIMINATION

Preventing the clogging of the metabolic machinery by its own waste products is the function of the excretory system. The kidneys show remarkable selective action in removing excessive amounts of salt, urea, and the like from the blood, while retaining useful substances like sugar and serum proteins. Other avenues of waste product elimination are the lungs, the skin, and the colon. Most of the contents of the lower bowel are not strictly waste products of cells, but indigestible portions of foodstuffs and the bodies of bacteria which live within the digestive tract. Psychobiologically, urination and defecation are the two important means of elimination, and the nervous controls of these two functions are very similar.

Retention of urine or feces leads to progressive toxic effects which if prolonged cause death. In infants, control of bladder and colon evacuation is reflex in nature. Distension of these organs provides an internal stimulus which in turn causes relaxation of the sphincter muscles, contraction of the circular and longitudinal muscles of the wall, and the expulsion of their contents. As the child matures he gradually acquires the ability to control these muscles and he urinates and defecates in prescribed places at prescribed times. In some human cultures the child is permitted to proceed at his own pace in developing control, but in American and European homes considerable parental effort goes into toilet training. Were it not for the emphasis placed upon developing habits of cleanliness, the function of elimination (like respiration) could be left completely to physiology. Some psychoanalytically oriented psychologists and psychiatrists consider that rigorous toilet training is a frequent factor in the production of emotional maladjustment, and advocate the more casual attitude of the South Sea Islanders. The intensity of the disciplinary measures inflicted is probably of much greater psychological significance than is the particular biological function which is involved. And the relationship works both ways: emotions also have profound effects upon the excretory organs.

In our culture there is something unclean about elimination; it is a function performed in private, the theme of questionable humor. Making elimination a private affair is defensible on grounds of sanitation and esthetics, but excessive rigidity concerning so strong a drive may lead to trouble. The colon and bladder can be affected by stimuli which have no specific relationship to the need of elimination, and prolonged emotional troubles can aggravate serious disorders in these organs, or even cause them.

It is interesting to note that some animals train themselves in sphincter control. Such lair-dwelling animals as cats and wolves do not usually foul their dens. On the contrary, the more intelligent monkey, whose natural habitat is the treetops and who has no permanent home, is not readily housebroken, nor are the domesticated beasts of the field, cattle or horses.

The psychological problems centering about the need for elimination of waste lie in the extent to which channelization and partial repression in one area may affect the whole personality. This is a subject on which there is a great deal of clinical opinion, but remarkably little animal experimentation. One reason is that the psychologist's favorite animals, rats and primates, are unsuited for experimental work in this field. Urination and defecation have been used by animal psychologists as indices of emotional disturbance, but this is about the limit of comparative studies.

[III]

Integrative Needs

AVOIDANCE OF TRAUMA

AN ORGANISM must avoid mechanical injury and extremes of heat or cold if it is to survive. Warnings of impending damage are provided by pain. The child learns that handling snow without mittens, stubbing his toe, and touching a pretty candle flame are all painful, and we are not surprised that he learns to avoid situations which have been associated with pain. Eventually he can be taught by precept and example to avoid dangerous substances and situations without putting them to actual test. He may become a scientist studying deadly bacteria, but he does not have to contract disease before he adopts sterile laboratory techniques.

There are important differences between pain and a drive such as hunger. The relief of the tissues from pain through a withdrawal reflex is much more abrupt than the relief of a tissue need for nutrients following eating, digestion, and absorption. The rapidity of drive reduction in escape from pain may explain why avoidance is so easily learned—often in one trial if the stimulus is intense enough.

In this discussion, pain is not considered as punishment, but escape from pain is considered to be a reinforcement. The distinction between these two views of pain may seem to be hairsplitting, but on the whole it is simpler theoretically to deal with only one principle of motivation, that of reinforcement. The act of withdrawing the finger from a flame is reinforcing, hence according to the above theory, a child will escape more quickly the next time he puts his finger in a flame. Actually, we know that he does better than that; he learns to keep his fingers away from hot objects. The punishment theory explains this by stating that punishment reduces the probability of the recurrence of behavior which leads to the punishment, in contrast to reward which increases the probability that behavior leading to reward will be repeated. The reinforcement-only theory has to take another way to explain the facts.

In order to do this we must postulate a drive which will be reduced by the *avoidance* of danger, just as the hunger drive is reduced by eating. Some birds have warning calls to which the young chicks appear to respond innately by going into hiding, but the human infant has to learn what is painful or dangerous through bitter experience. Admonitions to avoid danger are effective only after he has experienced real pain. Reinforcement theory identifies the drive behind avoidance behavior as fear. Like hunger and thirst, fear is associated with physiological changes within the body. These changes are responses to pain, but they can also be elicited by stimuli which have been associated with pain. The sight of the candle flame may still attract the attention of a child after he has been burnt, but now it produces a complex of responses which we call fear. By keeping at a distance from the flame he reduces the intensity of his fear. Similarly, he learns to avoid places or people which have been associated with pain.

Fear is labeled as an acquired or learned drive. Its physiological correlates are familiar: increased blood pressure and heart rate, sweat secretion, inhibition of digestive activity. There is both etymological and psychological relationship between the words *motivation* and *emotion*. Acquired drives, and fear in particular, are of great importance in current motivation theory, and are discussed in detail in a later section of this paper where arguments will be presented for regarding all emotional states as drive states.

SLEEP

In a nontechnical way, we define the state of sleep as one of generalized lower sensitivity to stimuli. Actually, there are gradations in depth of sleep, or to put it the other way, in degree of wakefulness. Even in sleep the organism has some ability to discriminate stimuli: a parent sleeps through heavy traffic noises, but wakes at the faint wail of an infant. The physiological nature of the need for sleep is uncertain. Forced wakefulness produces discomfort out of proportion to demonstrable changes in blood chemistry, or performance of psychomotor tasks. Following this phase, perceptions become grossly distorted and hallucinations are common. Eventually, it becomes impossible to keep awake even with drastic measures.

Recent neurological studies have shown that there

are sleep and wakefulness centers in the hypothalamus. Removal of the excitatory "waking" center in the posterior portion of the hypothalamus results in an animal which sleeps continuously. Removal of the inhibitory center in the anterior portion produces a permanent insomnia. The situation is exactly parallel to the control of eating by antagonistic hypothalamic centers.

Ordinarily individuals develop a cycle of sleep which corresponds to the twenty-four hour diurnal cycle. Sleep is easier in the dark because the level of stimulation is lower. People whose work requires a reversal of the common pattern can usually do so, but they revert to sleeping at night when they have free choice. One team of investigators went into the depths of Mammoth Cave and tried both to shorten to twenty hours or extend to twenty-eight hours the twenty-four hour cycle. A younger member of the group adjusted to different length days, but the cycle was too firmly built into the older members to be changed.

Probably it is more consistent to think of an activity or awareness drive than of a sleep drive. The infant spends most of the day asleep, but must wake at frequent intervals in order to eat. There is little differentiation in the newborn between the state of hunger and of wakefulness. As his nervous system matures, and as he learns more about the world, external stimuli take over a larger share of maintaining the state of wakefulness. In this view, sleep is regarded as the result of satiation of a drive for stimulation. A new type of stimulation counteracts sleepiness for a time, in the same way that a favorite delicacy can stimulate eating when one is satiated for ordinary food. But just as eventually continued eating results in satiation for all food, so eventually there is satiation for all forms of stimulation.

THE NEED FOR SEX

Already it has been stated that the heading for this section is a misnomer. Leuba (1954) cited several characteristics of biological needs which are not applicable to sex: ". . . it is not lifelong, its satisfaction is not necessary to individual survival, and at least in women there is no evidence of the sort of periodic internal changes that could give rise to sexual functioning in the absence of external stimulation." Yet no one can doubt that sex is a powerful drive, and that biological factors have something to do with it. If we look beyond the individual to his species, we recognize that sexual activity is essential to the maintenance of all the higher animals. To a great extent the social organization of a species depends upon its sexual cycle. In many birds, fish, and mammals sexual activity is highly seasonal; males and females may stay together only during this period. Sexual activity in man during the reproductive years is neither periodic nor seasonal, and this fact was undoubtedly important in the establishment of the first human families and tribes. Many economic and social forces mold contemporary family structure, but the permanent bond of sexual attraction is still of primary importance.

Although the fundamental patterns of sexual behavior in man are common to all mammals, there are some striking differences which represent the culmination of an evolutionary trend. One such trend is the increasing independence from hormonal control of the capacity for sexual excitation and sexual response. In such mammals as the rat, dog, mink, and other subprimate species, sexual activity, particularly in the female, is very rigidly determined by the amount of gonadal hormones in the blood. The sex interest of the female can be turned on and off by experimentally manipulating these hormones.

The subhuman primates, apes and monkeys, show some relationship between hormonal cycles and sexual behavior, but mating may occur in these species at times when reproduction is impossible. In man there is no definite relationship between physiological cycles and the strength of the sex drive. This is not to say that hormones have no influence in man. The growth of the genital organs, hence the capacity for full sexual experience, is controlled by the endocrine glands, and retardation of physical development is paralleled by slower psychosexual development. The flood of gonadal hormones at the age of puberty usually coincides with an upturn in interests in the opposite sex. But the strength and direction of these interests, and their maintenance, once they are established, are functions of the nervous system more than of the endocrine system.

The importance of learning in the integration of sexual responses is well shown in comparative studies on animals. Male rats and dogs usually copulate successfully on their first experience with a female in estrus. The prompt coordination and integration of the behavior patterns in the appropriate situation is evidence of instinctive control. In contrast, inexperienced male chimpanzees have been reported as unable to copulate successfully with inexperienced but sexually receptive females. These males and females had been isolated from each other since before puberty. Ordinarily juvenile chimpanzees participate in much pre-pubertal sex play, even though mating is delayed until maturity. Without such experience, hormones and normally adequate external stimulation do not suffice to·activate the total pattern.

Some interesting data on the interaction of experiential and maturational factors upon sex behavior have come from Harlow's (1962) studies on rhesus monkeys reared on "artificial mothers" constructed of wire mesh or cloth. Animals raised in this fashion were sexually incompetent as adults, although apparently normal with respect to hormones and other secondary sex characteristics. Although some of the "motherless" females were induced to mate after a long period of special training, the experimental males have never been observed to court and copulate normally, although some show signs of sexual interest. Particular kinds of contact experience early in life appear to be essential to effective psychosexual development in this species. Parental behavior is also impaired by the artificial system of rearing. Babies of motherless mothers are characteristically neglected. We must conclude that the survival of rhesus monkeys as a species is dependent upon the transmission of social behavior patterns from generation to generation, a process which takes place over the first few months of infant life.

At present it is uncertain whether such sexually incompetent individuals are wholly normal physiologically, but their difficulties appear to be primarily psychological. One should not conclude, however, that physiological drive states have nothing to do with sexual behavior. In human males, the accumulation of spermatozoa and of glandular secretions which make up seminal fluid provides an internal stimulus akin to the distension of the excretory organs by body wastes. The ejaculation of semen reduces this drive stimulus, and it is built up again gradually by secretory activity and storage of glandular products. This reflex mechanism may function to produce periodic nocturnal seminal emissions in the absence of any awareness of the event. As Leuba says, "At least physiologically, there is no such thing as a sexually frustrated male."

In the human female, the menstrual cycle is concerned with reproduction but not with sex drive. Human menstruation is a function quite different from heat or estrus in the lower mammals. Estrus serves to stimulate sexual activity in males so that copulation will occur at a time which coincides with the release of fertilizable eggs from the ovary. In humans this is left to chance. There is no *need* for the human female (nor for females of other species), insofar as reproduction is concerned, to experience orgasm during sexual intercourse. For the survival of the species, her role is only to stimulate the sexual reflexes of the male, and to provide a safe environment for the development of her offspring.

If the human female has achieved emancipation from hormonal control of sexual drive, and if she has no counterpart for the sexual tension produced in males by the accumulation of seminal fluid, we must look to learning and external stimuli as the source of her sexual motivation. Tactual stimulation of the genital areas is a powerful excitant, and produces a strong emotional response. Emotional responses can readily be conditioned to other stimuli associated with the primary excitant, and once aroused the emotion functions as a drive. The concept of pleasurable excitement as a learned drive is discussed in the section of this book dealing with acquired drives. The reasoning is exactly the same as that by which we developed the concept of fear as an acquired drive. If a drive must be learned, it will develop only insofar as opportunities for learning it are available. The Kinsey report (1953) indicated that there were great differences between women in the development of their sexual response capacity, and that in general these could be related to experiential factors.

The principles outlined above apply to males as well as females. The result is that in both sexes external stimuli become more and more important motivationally in comparison with internal drive stimuli. Just as the hunger drive is the matrix for a host of appetites for specific foodstuffs, so the sex drive is a basis for erotic appetites. The Kinsey group has reported that erotic pictures and literature are more stimulating to males than to females. This may be a biological difference, but it is more likely a function of differential training given to boys and girls.

In man, prepubertal sex play is strongly repressed in many cultures, and reliance may be placed upon verbal or written transmission of the habit pattern. Societies usually have rather formal codes regarding proper sex behavior, and the individuals with whom sex relations are permissible. Historically, these codes in our culture have been more restrictive on women

than on men. These rules have little to do with sex in
the biological sense, but are rather attempts to adjust
an individual's behavior to the structure of his society.
Homosexuality, auto-eroticism, and other practices
frowned upon in our culture are not deviations of a
drive, but habits which deviate from cultural norms.
A culture which sets out to encourage these activities
will be characterized by behavior we call abnormal.
In the long run, of course, no society can maintain
itself without providing for reproduction and discour-
agement of all but heterosexual habits. This is one of
the ways by which societies attempt to insure their
survival.

To summarize, there is an internal basis for sex
drive in human males but not in females. In both there
is evidence of the development of erotic appetites
based upon pleasurable responses to genital stimulation. Learning plays a major role in determining the
behavior adjustments which satisfy the appetites. Human beings are quite plastic in their psychosocial po-
tentialities, and auto-eroticism, homosexuality, and
normal heterosexual relationships are actually habits
acquired according to the laws of learning.

THE NEED FOR NURTURING

If it is misleading to write of a "need" for sex, it is
even more so to discuss a "need" for nurturing. Human
beings of both sexes can live their full span of years
without ever caring for a child. From the infant's point
of view there is a need for being nurtured, but this
can be largely if not completely broken down into the
requirements for metabolism and protection from in-

jury that we have already considered. Only if we shift
from a consideration of the individual to the species
as a whole can we justify the heading of this section.
Human babies and those of other mammals and birds
are always incapable of self-care at birth or hatching.
Survival of mammalian and avian species is dependent upon building into one or the other or both of the
parents a drive for attending to the helpless young.
Almost always the female assumes this function, although it is common in birds for the male to assist in
feeding. Male mammals are usually, but not always,
indifferent to the offspring they have sired. Since the
term maternal behavior refers only to the care given
by the mother, we shall employ the general term of
nurturant behavior to include participation by both
sexes and by other than the biological parents.

The nurturant drive, like the sex drive, is intimately
associated with hormones in many species of birds and
mammals. Injection of prolactin from the anterior
pituitary gland has been found to induce nest building, retrieving, and cuddling of newborn young in a
substantial proportion of virgin female rats. The full
effect appears to be dependent upon previous injections of female sex hormones. These hormones serve as
activators of the mating drive, and also as sensitizers
so that pituitary hormones which are produced later
are effective in eliciting and controlling maternal behavior.

Similar hormonal mechanisms probably exist in
other species of mammals and in birds, although de-
tailed studies are rare. Under domestication, which
involves selection for characteristics which are useful
to man but not necessarily to the animal concerned,

females of a species are commonly less strongly motivated to give maternal care than are their wild coun-
terparts.

Even in animals which seem to have maternal instincts activable by hormones, prior learning of a
general sort is sometimes essential to the giving of
adequate care to the young. In ring-doves, Lehrman
has found that males and females stimulate each other
by their presence in such a manner that hormones are
released which prepare the birds for incubating eggs.
Without social stimulation they will not sit on a nest
of eggs even after long exposure. The presence of
nest-building material and the response of nest building also affects the readiness for incubation behavior.
Thus, parental behavior can be demonstrated to be
dependent upon hormones, but the hormones are influenced by the behavior of the partner and by other
environmental stimuli. A particular endocrine gland
status and a specific set of stimuli are both essential
for the parental patterns to be expressed, but neither
factor by itself is a sufficient cause. Such motivation
is not classifiable as biogenic or psychogenic since it
is a composite of endogenous and exogenous forces.

Female rats raised under conditions in which they
had no objects of any kind to manipulate, no bedding,
no chunks of food, were greatly deficient in caring for
their own immature offspring. But rats, rabbits, cats,
dogs, reared in a reasonably varied environment generally care for their first litters in adequate fashion.
They clean the young, make nests for them, nurse
them, and vigorously attack any intruder. Among the
higher apes, the instinctive basis for infant care has
atrophied. Laboratory-reared chimpanzee mothers do

not give good care to their first babies, but improve on the second try. In wild colonies of monkeys, sexually immature animals of both sexes have been observed to give some care to infants, and this may establish habits which are useful later. In the primates, rather specific prior learning is apparently required for nurturant behavior.

It is doubtful whether any internal physiological basis for nurturant behavior exists in humans. A woman's hormones do change during pregnancy and following the birth of her child, but the importance of these is largely in connection with development of the uterus, and the functioning of the mammary glands. Taking the baby to breast and allowing him to suckle relieves the tension of milk accumulation, and may reinforce this particular part of the maternal pattern. There is no sound evidence, however, that the nurturant motive is any less strong among women who do not breast feed their children. The care of human infants depends not upon biological transmission of a hormone-sensitive instinctive pattern, but upon cultural transmission of social values. There is no reason to expect that the mere fact of motherhood or fatherhood will activate a strong motive leading to nurturant behavior. The motives must be implanted in each individual by his or her cultural traditions.

NEEDS FOR EXPLORATION AND MANIPULATION

If a hungry rat is put into a maze we are not surprised that it wanders along the alleys until it comes to a dish of food. One of the essential attributes of a drive is that it activates the animal. Now suppose we place a food-satiated animal into the same maze. He, too, will walk around sniffing the walls and eventually explore the entire available space. His activity will decline if he is kept in the same situation, but will rise again if he is placed in a different maze, or if he is taken out for a day and then replaced.

Rats and monkeys learn to repeatedly press a bar placed in their cage when the only reward is the opening of a door giving them the opportunity to investigate an adjacent space; or in the case of monkeys, the opportunity to observe a laboratory room through a window for thirty seconds at a time. Such behavior has obvious survival value, since knowledge of the surroundings may be essential for escape from danger. A rat walks around sniffing in corners, and gauging the width of passages by his whiskers, for his world is essentially one of contact and odor. Exploration for a human or a monkey may involve merely turning the eyeballs from side to side, for theirs is a visual world.

The reality of exploratory drive seems to be well accepted. Quoting Myers and Miller: "If an exploratory tendency can produce learning like other drives such as hunger, and also show a similar pattern of satiation and recovery, these functional parallels to already known drives would help to justify its classification in the same category with them, namely, as a drive."

Agreement has not been reached on whether exploratory drive is innate or acquired. It involves more than a tendency to orient to stimuli, for organisms actually acquire habits which lead to an increase in level of stimulation. It is a drive best shown in puppies, kittens, and young children to whom everything is new, and not as well in blasé adults. It has been observed as excessively strong in dogs which were reared under conditions of restricted stimulation. These animals brought into a room were incessantly active, and did not settle down following investigation of the room and its contents. The unusual deprivation of stimulation at early ages had a long-lasting effect on their motivation to explore.

There are interesting differences between exploratory drive and more conventional biological drives as hunger, thirst, and sex. Although an animal behaves as though it underwent deprivation and build-up of drive during confinement, and satiation and reduction of drive when the appropriate exploration has been carried out, it is hard to put one's finger on just where the deficit is and what satiation means. Something in the state of the brain rather than in the stomach, pharynx, or seminal vesicles is involved. Exploration is more easily repressed than is behavior motivated by the biological drives, though it should be noted that exploratory behavior is also part of the total response pattern motivated by hunger, thirst, and sexual arousal. Thus special precautions are necessary to observe exploratory drive in "pure" form.

A point may be made about the role of learning in acquiring an exploratory drive. If the drive were simply part of the response to hunger, then space-restricted animals would not learn it, because they never have to explore to find food. Instead of being less exploratory, they are more so, and this fact suggests that exploration is just as innate as drinking and eating.

Few, if any, experimental observations on exploratory drive have dealt with humans. Since it is a cerebral rather than an endocrine drive, one would expect it to be well developed in man according to the principle that man's central nervous system is more autonomous than that of the lower vertebrates. Furthermore, the reduction of the intensity of deprivation states associated with the metabolic drives results, in the case of civilized man, in relatively more influence of nonmetabolic drives and appetites. We conclude that exploratory drive could be an important source of human motivation.

Closely related to exploration is the manipulation of objects. Harlow and his colleagues have demonstrated that monkeys improve their performance in solving mechanical puzzles (opening hooks, unlocking hasps, etc.) when their learning is motivated by no reward other than the privilege of taking the device apart. Similar mechanical puzzles have a strong fascination for humans of all ages. Since man's manipulative ability and fine finger movements are so highly developed it is likely that this particular drive is best shown in humans, but it has been little studied.

Perhaps manipulatory drive is simply a specialized form of a more general drive for animals to utilize their full repertory of motor skills. The play activities of birds and mammals have obvious biological usefulness in training for adult functions, but one cannot credit either the young or their parents with foreknowledge of this. Recognition of a drive for motor expression obviates the necessity of multiplying the number of drives to take care of such specific behaviors as otters sliding down mud banks into the water, or cats playing with balls of yarn.

Exploratory and manipulative drives are really complementary tendencies, one toward increased perceptual activity, the other toward increased motor activity. We shall adopt the adjective *expressive* to designate all such drives and the term *preemptive* to refer to the "strong" drives which supersede them in emergencies. Responses to expressive drives are easily inhibited by pain, fatigue, or fear.

Our class of expressive drives appears to be identical with White's (1959) concept of *competence*. This writer, reacting to a discontent with theories of motivation based upon primary drives and their derivatives, has used competence to refer to a common property of visual exploration, activity, and manipulation. The thesis is proposed "that all of these behaviors have a common biological significance; they all form part of the process whereby the animal or child learns to interact effectively with his environment."

These ideas broaden the concept of needs to include more than food, water, and the avoidance of trauma. Organisms, at least those with more than a rudimentary nervous system, need information about their environment just as they need sources of energy. And the means of gathering information is built into the functioning organism. Whether the motives included in White's category of competence should be considered as drives is perhaps a matter of taste. At present, the hunger for information has not been related to physiology in the same way as hunger for food. Yet the neural processes underlying satiation with food may be very much like those which impel us eventually to turn away from a beautiful view, or to rise and turn off the radio which is playing a popular song just once too often.

There is a curious and perhaps fundamental difference between expressive and preemptive drives. If a rat runs a maze under a preemptive drive, say hunger or thirst, he eventually learns to take the most direct path to the goal. Learning involves obtaining the maximum reinforcement with the least effort. If the rat persists in entering many cul-de-sacs, we are apt to conclude that he is not very intelligent. In arriving at this conclusion, we are tacitly assuming that the path of least effort is the one that any sensible rat should take. There is no logical basis for this assumption. In fact, the experiments on expressive drives show that animals will work harder than it seems they need to. The principle of least effort works in many situations, but it is not an established law of behavior. A principle of optimal effort, which is higher than minimum, may prove to be more general.

One may venture a guess that in animals with a well-developed cerebral cortex (carnivores and primates), the expressive drives take over a larger and larger role in motivation. These animals take care of their preemptive drives very efficiently with as little effort as possible. The main business of their life, particularly in youth, is reinforcing their expressive drives. This applies with major emphasis to the human primate, and the reader may be interested in trying to apply this idea to such activities as sports, scientific research, music, and art.

Innate and
Acquired Drives

THE PRECEDING ARGUMENTS on the relationship between behavior and needs may be briefly summarized. The behavior of an organism *must* result in the satisfaction of its biological needs if the organism is to survive. To insure the survival of a species, the behavior repertory of a sexually reproducing species *must* provide for the combination of male and female germ cells, and frequently the protection of offspring until they can care for themselves. Provision of care is not necessary if fertilized eggs are produced sufficient in number to replace the parents in spite of high mortality. Matching behavior to needs involves utilization of environmental cues to direct behavior toward suitable goals. In many animals, specific cues presented to a physiologically primed organism may trigger off complicated actions such as courtship and mating without a prolonged period of learning. However, a general evolutionary trend is seen in the higher mammals which results in a decrease in the importance of innate stimulus-response connections, at least for complex responses, and an increase in the importance of learning the reinforcement contingencies of various stimuli.

To explain the fact that stimuli vary in their ability to elicit behavior at different times, we have used the term *drive* to designate a state of the organism which affects its motivation. Drive is not synonymous with motivation, for the latter is the result of interaction between the drive state and the particular cues which are present. Many of the factors such as hormone concentration and blood sugar concentration which affect responsiveness are not stimuli in the ordinary sense of the word, but are chemical conditions which facilitate or depress the excitability of nerve cells. Each need which requires special responses for its satisfaction is potentially the basis for goal-directed activity. The more promptly a need can generate a drive state, and the more directly the drive results in goal oriented behavior, the greater will be the benefit to the animal for the same expenditure of energy. It is not necessary that the need-drive-goal relationship be innately determined, nor that it be consciously conceived. Thus far we have dealt with behavior directly concerned with providing water, energy containing foods, or escape from pain. Now we wish to extend the drive concept to a wider range of goals, including eventually the highest aspirations of mankind. This requires that we summarize the properties of drives systematically, so that we can have criteria for characterizing acquired drives.

(1) A drive state sensitizes an organism to particular cues, and perhaps to stimulation in general.

(2) Drive-motivated-behavior sequences terminate when a goal is attained and the drive is reduced.

Drives are named according to the mode by which they are terminated, by food, water, sexual orgasm, relief of pain.

(3) Drive termination or reduction strengthens immediately antecedent stimulus-response bonds. This is probably a sufficient condition, and is possibly an essential condition for learning. Hence, an important method of demonstrating acquired drives is to use one learned response as the reinforcing basis of new learning.

(4) Drive states are associated with internal physiological conditions of the organism which are in part specific for each type of drive. Ultimately the drive state must be referred to the nervous system, but it can frequently be related to activities of the viscera or chemistry of the blood. The fact that some drives are not associated with such peripheral changes is not proof that they have no physiological correlates. As yet much of the central nervous system is inaccessible to study except under highly artificial conditions in which drive states would not be found. Current research with implanted electrodes and intracerebral injections is, however, leading to a more direct attack on the neurological bases of drives.

If we are going to talk about acquired drives they must be fitted into the descriptive scheme outlined above. Acquired drives, in addition, must be shown to depend upon learning, and the conditions of learning should be specified. Acquired drives have a dual character, being both responses and intervening variables between stimuli and other responses. The distinction between an acquired drive and a habit may not always be clear-cut, but provisionally we may consider that a habit is an accustomed way of reaching a goal, while an acquired drive is a determinant of the nature of the goal. There are critics of the drive theory who advocate the functional autonomy of well-established habits, and claim that organisms continue to do what they have been doing without regard for the reinforcing consequences of their actions. Under this view, it seems necessary to postulate some additional principle to account for the occasional survival of apparently nonreinforced habits.

One can approach the subject of acquired drives with two distinct attitudes. Mankind obviously is impelled by many motives, often by several at a time. Men seek fame, power, love, social groups, money, canceled postage stamps, scientific principles. We might multiply the number of drives indefinitely to cover all types of activities. On the other hand, we might try to categorize these diverse behaviors under a few major drives. The extreme of the second attitude would be to consider even the most complex behavior as motivated directly by basic biological needs. In this paper we shall adopt an intermediate position: that there are a limited number of acquired drives which play an active part in human motivation. These are the conditions of the organism we call *emotions*. This view implies that man and the lower animals are much alike in their basic drives, and that the motivational differences between them are functions of man's superior discriminatory ability, and his capacity for stimulation by symbolic representation of physical stimuli, that is by words and pictures.

EMOTIONS AS ACQUIRED DRIVES

Historically, emotion has been variously treated according to four main points of view: the introspective with emphasis on conscious content; the dynamic typified by Freud and widely adopted in psychiatry and psychosomatic medicine; the physiological which is concerned with bodily changes; and the behavioristic which defines emotion in terms of measurable effects upon responses. We shall draw primarily upon the behavioristic and physiological approaches in considering emotions as acquired drives. There is a rich literature on emotional behavior in man and animals, and a considerable divergence of opinion which will be neglected in favor of presenting a consistent theory of the motivational aspects of emotion.

Emotion is not something set apart from the realm of unemotional behavior. One dimension of emotion is activation, and at any given moment one exists at a level ranging between deep sleep and a violent frenzy of rage. Intermediate degrees of activity can be placed somewhere on an intensive scale of emotionality. Defining qualitative variation in emotion is not easy, particularly if one adheres to the behavioristic approach. Traditionally, fear, anger, happiness, and sometimes disgust are recognized as major emotions, often on the basis of subjective reports, but these are not clearly separated in their physiological manifestations. The motivational model adopted here distinguishes between emotional states not by subjective reports or physiological patterns, but on the basis of the kind of behavior which will reduce their intensity. Just as hunger drive is identified by observing that it facilitates behavior which is terminated when the hungry organism eats, fear can be defined as the drive state which is reduced by avoiding a specific stimulus. Or, if avoidance is not possible, the fear drive produces a response of inactivation and concealment. Similarly, anger is reduced by aggressive behavior directed toward objects or individuals; pleasure by approaching, contacting, and otherwise seeking stimulation through the many sensory pathways; disgust by removal of the eliciting stimulus from the environs. The most thoroughly studied of the acquired drives is fear, and it will be considered first.

Fear

Fear is easily induced experimentally in animals, usually by electric shock which is painful but leaves no harmful aftereffects at the levels employed. It is also an important human drive, one which is frequently in conflict with other sources of motivation. Many controls on antisocial behavior operate through fear of the consequences of acts which are proscribed by the social code. In neurotic individuals it is common to find a generalized fear which has no definite external sources. Such internalized obsessive fear is called anxiety.

Fear, like other acquired drives, is a response as well as a drive. Pain, sudden withdrawal of support, loud sounds, and under certain circumstances almost any unfamiliar stimulus, can produce this emotional response. Years ago the physiological components of fear were described by W. B. Cannon and his co-workers. They observed a mass arousal of the sympathetic division of the autonomic nervous system and

increased discharge of the hormone epinephrine from
the adrenal gland. As a result, heart rate and blood
pressure rose, digestive processes were inhibited, the
pupils dilated, sugar was released into the blood, and
the electrical conductivity of the skin was increased.
Not all of these reactions were equally intense in every
person, and there was considerable individuality in
the pattern of responses. Cannon considered the
changes as adaptive, since they prepared the organism
for vigorous activity, flight, or fight, which was apt
to be required in situations where pain was inflicted.

A model for the development of the physiological
response to the status of a drive will now be presented
in five diagrams with explanatory notes. Diagram 1
describes the innate responses of an organism to a
painful stimulus.

DIAGRAM 1

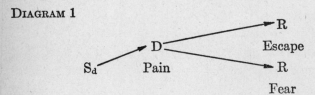

In this diagram S_d represents a nocuous agent such
as electric shock, extreme heat, or mechanical injury.
Pain is regarded as a drive state leading to responses
of fear and escape. Actually, we should write multiple
R's for each of these, since the individual may try
several ways of escaping, and the word fear implies a
host of individual responses organized into a characteristic pattern. If the subject tries several ways of
escaping, but only one is effective, we should expect
him to eventually develop a fixed escape habit. We
can also write multiple S's on the left hand side of the
diagram.

In Diagram 2, S_d is still a primary agent producing pain, but S_n is a neutral stimulus which is presented just previously or simultaneously.

DIAGRAM 2

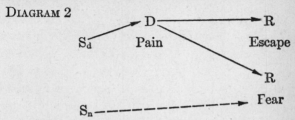

S_n may be the appearance of the nocuous agent, or in the laboratory it might be a warning buzzer signifying an impending shock (S_d). If a suitable experiment is performed, a rat can learn to avoid shock altogether, provided there is an interval between S_n and S_d long enough to allow an avoidance response to occur.

The avoidance habit is more easily established if the rat has an opportunity to avoid shock altogether than if he is exposed to an inevitable pairing of S_d and S_n. This seems reasonable, for making a response which will not prevent shock is less useful than making a response which will prevent shock. Nevertheless, according to the general theory of learning we have adopted, one would expect that learning would be better when it is reinforced, and escape from pain is a strong reinforcement. What serves as reinforcement for a rat's learning when it experiences no pain, and what is the drive which maintains an avoidance habit for long periods without the need for additional shock? One explanation is that fear may serve both as a response and as a drive, and that reinforcement occurs when fear is reduced. This is shown in Diagram 3

in which S_n is now designated as S_c, a conditioned
stimulus rather than a neutral one.

DIAGRAM 3

In Diagram 3 the response of avoidance takes the
subject away from S_n, thus reducing the drive of fear.
In early stages of habit development obvious signs of
fear may be present. Later the avoidance habit may
be carried out with no overt symptoms of emotional
disturbance. However, if the avoidance response is
blocked for any reason, an emotional response may
reappear in full force.

Diagrams 4 and 5 go even further. The avoidance
response of Diagram 4 is an "anticipatory-drive-reduc-
ing response." Because it takes some time for the
physiological symptoms of fear to develop, it is possible to conceal the nature of the latent drive motivating the avoidance behavior.

DIAGRAM 4

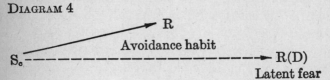

DIAGRAM 5

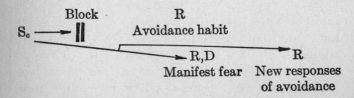

In Diagram 5 the anticipatory response is blocked, the latent drive becomes manifest, and new responses are given.

In these two diagrams one can find an explanation for the persistence of avoidance habits after they may have outlived their original usefulness. In stage 4, the subject never has an opportunity to learn that an avoidance habit is no longer serving to protest from a nocuous stimulus. Stage 5 represents a case of "reality testing." Since avoidance is impossible, the latent fear response becomes active and is thus exposed to extinction if not paired with an S_d.

A simple example serves to illustrate the application of the latent drive principle to human motivation. The worker with x-rays is careful to avoid exposure, although the pain which such radiation can produce may be delayed many years until the victim has a serious case of skin cancer. In such cases it may be difficult to identify an emotional response as the drive motivating the careful practice of the x-ray operator. Suppose that he suddenly learns that the shielding which he thought was perfectly adequate has actually been allowing dangerous amounts of radiation to pass. The situation shifts from that of Diagram 4 to Diagram 5 and the latent fear drive becomes manifest.

Stimuli other than pain can serve as S_d in the diagrams above. The quality of unfamiliarity is so important in the genesis of fear that it merits special mention. Strangeness depends upon learning, for an individual must have learned something about one environment before he can compare another with it and find it strange and frightening. There is now abundant evidence that certain fears often may be based more upon strangeness and unpredictability than upon specific learning experiences. For example, strong emotional reactions were aroused in juvenile chimpanzees confronted with snakelike objects, models of human or chimpanzee heads detached from the body, and other bizarre objects not common in the environs of the apes. These objects did not arouse fear in infant chimpanzees which had not reached a suitable degree of sophistication. Similar responses can be observed in dogs which are kennel raised and have limited acquaintance with the wide variety of shapes, odors, and sounds which make up the world. When brought into a new situation these animals appear to be frightened by specks of dust, an overhanging beam, a squeaky door, or the odor of a strange dog. The capacity for such fear is a function of intellectual development, and must be reckoned as one of the hazards of an improved cerebral cortex. The phenomenon is quite different from the releaser function described by the ethologists (see section on ethology). It is not an innate response to a particular stimulus, nor the conditioning of a neutral stimulus by pairing with a nocuous one. Perhaps the most general explanation would be that a stimulus which is strong enough to produce arousal will ordinarily elicit a definite habitual response, but if it fails to do so it will activate fear.

The foregoing is not meant to imply that cultural imitation and specific instruction play no part in fears of humans. Because of human capacity for conceptualization, it is possible to develop strong avoidance behavior which is very remotely associated with pain, withdrawal of support, or unfamiliarity. Thus we may avoid drinking from a common cup, exposure to x-rays, or playing with dynamite caps, although none of these have caused us personal injury. However, such complexity affects the S_c side of our diagrams rather than modifying the R and D relationships. Between the rat in the shock box, and man in the modern world, lies a great gulf in perception, memory, and capabilities for motor responses, but the role of fear as an acquired drive is probably very much alike in both.

There have been many laboratory studies on the function of fear as an acquired drive for the learning of new habits. The Miller box is a device which has been much used for this purpose. It has two compartments, one painted white and the other black. The floor of the white compartment is a metallic grid which can be electrified. A door which can be opened and closed by the experimenter, or by certain actions of the animal subject, is placed between the compartments. In one experiment it was demonstrated that rats had no preference for either side when they could move freely through the open door. They were then shocked in the white portion of the apparatus with the door closed. On subsequent trials they would run rapidly from the white to the black compartment, although no further shocks were administered. After the avoidance habit, motivated by an acquired fear of the white compartment, was well developed, the door was closed and latched by a device which a rat could release by turning a wheel placed in the white compartment. Rats placed on the white side with the door closed behaved in an agitated manner. Eventually, most subjects turned the wheel which lowered the door and permitted them to go into the black compartment. The habit of wheel turning was acquired without giving the animals any further shocks in the white compartment. In a continuation of the experiment, control of the door was shifted from the wheel to a bar which projected into the wire cage. Still without giving additional shocks, the rats transferred their habit from the now nonfunctional wheel to bar pressing. This experiment demonstrates that, even in the lowly rat, new learning can be built upon an acquired fear without the necessity of reintroducing the primary drive stimulus of pain.

In introducing the subject of acquired drives, four descriptive criteria of the drive state were listed. It is interesting to see whether the experiment with rats in the Miller box allows us to classify fear as a drive with essentially the same characteristics as hunger or thirst. The subjects of the experiment were sensitized to respond to particular stimuli associated with the white box. This experiment by itself does not tell us whether they have been sensitized to whiteness in general, or only white sides of Miller boxes. Exposing the animal to these stimuli activates a sequence of actions which is terminated when it escapes from the white side. The responses may be as varied as running, or wheel turning or bar pressing and they terminate when the drive stimuli are no longer present. The subjects learn to behave in the manner which is most effective in allowing them to escape, and are able to change their habits in accordance with the principle that stimulus-response connections which immediately precede drive reduction will be reinforced. Finally, although the Miller experiment was not particularly concerned with physiological effects, it is certain from large bodies of data from similar experiments that there were profound alterations in almost every organ of the rat's body.

Although fear is of lifelong importance, and is the basis for learning many new habits, one must not lose sight of the fact that it is a response as well as a drive. Hence, it is subject to extinction like any other responses if it does not serve to reduce a drive. This can be verified from ordinary experience. A woman working in her kitchen is generally careful to avoid handling hot objects. Occasionally she may become careless and receive a burn. Following such an experience it is observable that her habits of care are unusually strong for a time. A near accident while driving a car will result in extra-cautious driving for a time, although in this case the strengthening of the fear response is based upon an imaginary rather than an actual injury. Such ideational reinforcements are particularly human, and depend upon the great extension of conceptualization made possible by language.

Rage

Since the subject of fear as an acquired drive has been treated in some detail, it will be possible to be more brief in our discussion of rage. The response is not always dissimilar to fear, and the separation between the two states is not a sharp one either behaviorally, physiologically, or subjectively. The angry person is traditionally red-faced, the frightened one, pale, but in both there is a mobilization of energy-release mechanisms of the body for flight or fight.

Some recent studies suggest that the physiological features of fear are similar to those produced by the hormone epinephrine; those of rage to the closely related norepinephrine, but many of the effects of these hormones are similar.

Anger may arise from several causes, many of which overlap with fear. Pain and unfamiliar stimuli may arouse either state alternately. Perhaps the most important cause is a restriction of activity or the blocking of a response in a strongly motivated animal. The intensity of the anger response is a function of the strength of the drive whose satisfaction is frustrated. The conditions for producing this drive state are depicted in Diagrams 6-10.

DIAGRAM 6

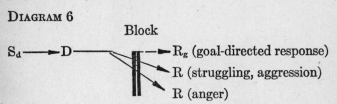

In Diagram 6 S_d, as before, represents any primary drive stimulus leading to any drive, D. The goal-directed response R_g is blocked, and there are no other available responses which will be successful (or at least the individual concerned cannot find them). These are the conditions which elicit anger and aggression.

Diagram 7 represents the pairing of a previously neutral stimulus with the blockade, and in Diagram 8 we see that this stimulus now arouses anger even in the absence of any real frustration, and leads to aggressive behavior. If the principle of anticipatory

DIAGRAM 7

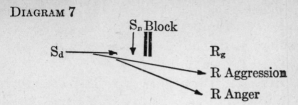

DIAGRAM 8

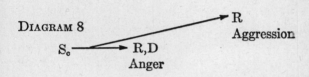

DIAGRAM 9

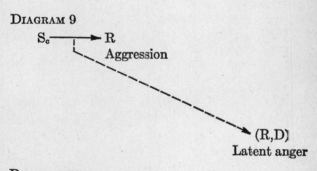

DIAGRAM 10

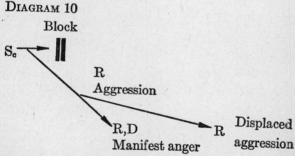

drive-reducing responses applies to anger, the aggressive habit may be maintained for a time without any particular overt signs of anger. But if the habitual aggression is itself blocked, manifest anger and new responses, possibly aggression displaced against some previously neutral object or individual, will occur.

Laboratory study of the genesis and development of anger as an acquired drive has been neglected as compared with fear. This is perhaps due to the fact that anger is most often manifested in social situations which present experimental difficulties.

Aggression, both personal and social, is one of the major problems of mankind, and much effort is expended in attempting to control it. If the theory presented here has merit, solutions may be attempted at two points: (1) the elimination of frustration, and (2) the substitution of response habits motivated by anger (either manifest or latent) which will not be socially harmful.

Let us apply the diagrams above to a hypothetical situation, a composite of many maladjusted families. In this case, severe restrictive parental discipline constantly blocks a child's goal-directed behavior. If the child wants something he does not have, no effort is made to provide a substitute goal. In such a situation, the parent becomes the S_c of Diagram 8, and the parent's presence arouses anger because it involves frustration. The child's aggression toward the parent may take the form of actual blows, or may be expressed in epithets or disobedience. At the stage of Diagram 9, the habits of aggression have become so well entrenched that the latent emotional states are not obvious. As the child grows older, he is subjected to many influences which tend to suppress open display of aggression toward other people. In particular, he is taught that one should treat one's parents with respect. The drive is still present, however, and may now motivate habits of aggression toward younger and weaker children or toward animals.

This example is not intended to convey the idea that parents should never discipline their children. A good parent is a source of both reward and restraint to a child. A parent who gives abundant affection to a child can give effective discipline without inducing a habitual aggressive reaction in his child, because the S_c for aggression is not the person of the parent, but the particular situation which requires disciplinary action. The student may be interested in seeing how well these diagrams fit other instances of aggressive behavior, social climbing and racial discrimination, for example.

Pleasure

We are accustomed to think of pleasure as a response to stimulation rather than as a drive for action. A little consideration will show that, like fear or anger, it is both a response and a drive. There is a great deal of truth in the popular saying that pleasure is in anticipation. Going to a dance or to a football game is the response that lowers the pleasure drive. We expect that a drive will be less intense following the satisfaction of the need which gives rise to it. Pleasure as a drive seems to have been much more neglected by experimental psychologists than fear and anger. Perhaps this is because behaviorists have tried to eliminate subjective concepts from their science;

for example, they substitute the neutral word "reinforcement" for the evaluative word "reward." Hebb
is one of the few who has been concerned with the
nature of pleasure as a neurophysiological phenomenon, and as a source of motivation. Recent experiments
with electrodes implanted in the brain have led Olds
to postulate pleasure and displeasure centers. Animals
will work to obtain electrical stimulation of particular
brain regions just as they will work to obtain food.
Although details are far from clear, outlines of a
neurological theory of reinforcement are apparent.
Among the complications is the fact that rats will
alternatively turn stimulations on and then off when
electrodes are properly placed.

Fundamentally, the development of pleasure as an
acquired drive parallels the course of the more dramatic emotions, fear and anger. Pleasurable excitement
is found as an accompaniment of drive-reducing responses of many kinds. Signs of emotional arousal are
vividly seen in the eating and play behavior of babies
and of young puppies. Sexual activity is highly emotional. The pleasure response, at first inseparable from
the drive-reducing response, can become independently conditioned to the stimuli which have been
associated with the drive-reducing response. Now the
odors and sight of food elicit the same pleasurable
excitement which was originally a response to eating.
This is shown in Diagram 11 which is comparable to

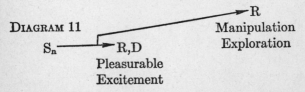

DIAGRAM 11

S_n ⟶ R,D
Pleasurable
Excitement

R
Manipulation
Exploration

Diagrams 2 and 7. Pleasurable excitement as a drive leads to the same kind of responses that we have associated with the expressive drives of manipulation and exploration, drives which lead to an increase in stimulation rather than a decrease. In other words, there are certain kinds of stimulation, tactual, visual, auditory, thermal, gustatory, which are capable of producing a level of excitement in the nervous system which is called pleasant. Hebb theorizes that this level of excitement is favorable for the functional organization of groups of nerve cells into larger units called phase sequences. The element of novelty is important for the arousal of pleasure, since eating the most delicious food or looking at a delightful scene becomes unpleasant if continued too long. One could postulate that the food had lost its attraction after it had reduced a hunger drive. Likewise, one could suggest that beautiful scenery reduces a hunger for stimulation and novelty. A great variety of experiences are innately able to satisfy this "hunger," and through learning it is possible to condition almost any stimulus to the pleasure drive. In simple terms, getting pleasure out of something produces a drive to manipulate, taste, explore, listen to, or look at the eliciting stimulus, and when this is done the capacity of the stimulus to arouse pleasure is temporarily lost.

By a process of gradually pushing the responses forward (the principle of anticipatory response) overt manifestations of pleasurable excitement become less apparent. Old dogs are less volatile than puppies, and middle-aged alumni more restrained than college students. The alumni may have accepted a different role in society which requires them to behave in a dignified manner, but it is doubtful if an old hound dog is responding to cultural influences when he acquires a sedate manner. But there is less novelty in an old dog's life, and consequently fewer overt manifestations of emotional arousal.

We would expect the latent drive state motivating pleasurable habits to become manifest when the habit is blocked, and this appears to be true. However, the response is not likely to be as violent as when a latent fear drive is made manifest. We manifest annoyance when we cannot obtain our favorite brand of coffee at the grocery; we become frightened and angry when we are detained by a traffic snarl from an appointment with an impatient and important personage.

Actually, there seem to be two types of pleasures, Pleasure 1 and Pleasure 2, separated both psychologically and physiologically. In the preceding sections we have been discussing Pleasure 1, an emotional state of excitement and heightened awareness of the world about which operates as a drive toward activity. The physiological accompaniments of this state are somewhat similar to those of fear and anger, namely manifestations of sympathetic nervous system discharge. Pleasure 2 involves decreased excitability and a preponderance of parasympathetic nervous system activity. It is a state of relaxation which follows a heavy meal, the relief of sexual tension, or rest after vigorous activity. As compared with Pleasure 1, it is toward the opposite end of the arousal intensity continuum; between Pleasures 1 and 2 lies a common neutral condition with which all emotional states are contrasted.

In summary, emotions may be regard...
of response which serve a motivational...
view has become increasingly popular, alth...
contrasting opinion that emotions are disrupti...
tors in behavior still has its supporters, and under s...
circumstances is true. If one is trying to teach a chi...
to multiply, or a rat to jump to a triangle rather than
a circle, a strong fear reaction in the subject disrupts
the learning process. But both child and rat learn
very well when they are frightened. The trouble is
that what they learn is inappropriate to the situation
as viewed by the teacher. The habits of avoidance
established under these strong drives are not easily
changed, and are often incompatible with multiplica-
tion or with form discrimination. The central problem
of educating human beings seems to be the proper
use of the emotions as sources of motivation for
socially desirable behavior. The diagrams which have
been presented are schemes which have been greatly
simplified for purposes of exposition. In a laboratory
situation it may be possible to manipulate events so
that there is a single S_d, say electric shock, and a
single S_c, say the sound of a buzzer, but in life situations S_d and S_c are constellations of circumstances.
Long chains of association may result in a conditioned
stimulus which is removed by many steps from any
primary fear-inducing stimulus. Yet, if our theory has
any validity, the early conditioning of emotional responses will have far reaching consequences for the
motivational structure of an adult. His attitudes and
values will in final analysis depend upon fear, pleasure, or anger experienced sometime in the past.

on in Social
Situations

MEN LIVE in communities, in social groups within communities, and in families. Much of their behavior is oriented toward other persons, rather than toward inanimate objects. We speak of such motivations as envy, jealousy, love, pride, respect, and patriotism. Some behavior is facilitated in social situations. We talk and laugh when other people are about, and much less often when alone. We are apt to eat more when in good company than in solitude. Other behavior is inhibited in groups, sometimes because of cultural taboos (sex, elimination) and sometimes because of the distractions inherent in group interaction. Creative workers need isolation since they are dealing with imagery, and motives based on recall of stimulus traces have a hard time in competition with those based on direct sensory processes.

Because human beings are universally social it was formerly considered that they had an instinct of gregariousness. Nowadays the theory of instincts, at least in humans, is in disfavor, but there is a possibility that innate qualities in man make him relatively susceptible to socialization. At any rate, the long dependence of human children upon parental care affords ample opportunity for the parents to reward the child by caring for his needs and giving him an opportunity to reduce drive tensions. Miller and Dollard in their book, *Social Learning and Imitation,* have discussed this subject in great detail.

In Miller and Dollard's formulations emphasis is placed on the role of acquired drives in the development of affectional behavior in infants, and particular stress is laid upon the parental functions of feeding and providing relief from discomfort. Experiments with infant monkeys by Harlow have shown that affectional behavior is based as much or more upon contact comfort. Baby monkeys raised on "artificial mothers" developed stronger social bonds with cloth models, which were not provided with a food source, than with wire models which gave milk but were more hard and unyielding to touch. Undoubtedly, acquired drives based upon the preemptive needs of the organism and expressive drives based upon innate reinforcing properties of stimulation both contribute to the development of social behavior. In nature the two sources of motivation are usually complementary, but in the laboratory we can set them in opposition and produce disruptions of social relationships. In human families, too, we find examples of dissociation between these types of motivation and observe social maladjustment of children reared under such conditions.

A survey of comparative sociology shows that even closely related animal species may vary greatly in the amount of social organization which they develop.

The moose, a member of the deer tribe native to North America and Europe, is usually solitary. Almost the only associations between these animals are courtship and copulation of male and female in the mating season, fighting between males during the same period, and the care of the calf by the mother. This minimal social organization is in sharp contrast to the closely related American elk which lives in large herds and migrates and feeds in groups. Similar variations in the size and permanence of social groups can be found in other vertebrate classes from fish to fowl. The existence of groupings not directly dependent upon sexual or nurturant drives has led some biologists to postulate a drive for social stimulation. Others would consider gregariousness as a habit based upon the more efficient satisfaction of needs by groups than by individuals alone. Allee and his co-workers have emphasized the benefits of communal life, but the fact that group life is advantageous does not explain why an individual elk becomes herd-oriented while a moose does not.

In many species of fish and birds there appear to be built-in responses to particular stimuli provided by other members of species, and these innate responses are the basis of social organization. Experience, and especially early experience, is of comparable importance for the socialization of mammals. If strangeness is a stimulus for fear, and if the familiar environment always contains other animals of the same species, then isolation will produce a fear drive which is reduced by approaching another animal. Opposing socialization are such forces as pain inflicted by group members upon each other, and group interference with the reinforcement of its members (e.g., in competition over food). The balance between socializing and nonsocializing influences is delicate, and even breeds within a species may differ in their ability to form orderly social groups. In one experiment, littermate dogs (4 to 6 per group) were placed in large exercise pens where they could develop their own social organization. In some breeds, the dominant animals drove out the weaker members, while others were more tolerant and lived together in relative peace. These observations indicate that extreme intragroup aggressiveness is a disruptive factor in social organization, and that this is partially under hereditary control. Species differences in gregariousness could result from variation in the relative ease of eliciting the responses of avoidance and aggression.

Another process which is important to social organization is *imprinting*. Lorenz has described how geese tend to follow the first large object which they encounter after hatching, and how they continue to do so for the rest of their lives. In nature, goslings imprint on another goose, but experimentally they can be imprinted by some other bird, a man, or even a green cube. Possibly the permanence and irreversibility of imprinting has been overemphasized, and it may be really a form of learning subject to similar laws. The point is that first learning has certain advantages over later learning, since there is less interference from contradictory habits. Social stimulation and social rewards at the time when associative learning is first possible are of critical importance for later social responses. In species with precocious young (sheep, goats), associative learning is possible at birth, and a lamb reared by humans away from the flock learns to prefer humans to sheep. In puppies, the capacity for associative learning appears later, and introduction into a human society is successful at the age of four to six weeks, at which age the lamb would have been well assimilated into the sheep flock and difficult to attract away from its own species. Puppies allowed to run wild for four months are much more difficult to train than at an earlier age. In all species which have been investigated, periods of enhanced sensitivity to socialization have been found. Scott calls them critical periods of socialization.

Turning to humans, motivation to seek companionship may be based upon two main kinds of learning. First, a person may discover that his biological needs and his appetitive goals can be secured with less effort if he cooperates with other people. Secondly, he may be fearful, and find that fear is reduced by the presence of other people or of specific persons. It should be easy for the student to deduce that the relative importance of these two forms of motivation will make a great deal of difference as to the kind of social relationships which an individual develops. In one case, social relationships will be directed toward reaching common goals. In the fear-motivated relationships, habits will be directed toward keeping close to the person who relieves the fear, not toward mutual objectives.

Man is a social animal, it is true, but each one of us must be socialized anew without the benefit of built-in instincts which will function appropriately in every situation. Once committed to an elaborate culture (and remember that the most primitive humans have language, religion, fire, tools) man's survival depends upon his becoming socialized in each generation. Within the limits set by biological needs in the narrow sense, the emotional and expressive drives can be developed in a variety of ways to insure good social habits. This is the great task of education.

Several of the founders of modern psychology, notably James and McDougall, ascribed to animals and man as many different instincts as they considered necessary to account for the various persistent goal-directed responses which each species demonstrated. Instinctive behavior was due to setting off certain chains of responses by appropriate internal and external stimuli. The behavioristic revolt in psychology displaced the concept of instinct with that of drive. As Irwin says, "Instincts imply that the organism is innately prepared to do the right thing when a need-state arises; drives imply that the organism is impelled to learn what to do." Like most revolutions, this one went too far in denying the possibility of innate determinants of behavior. The same stringent scientific criteria must be applied to explanations based upon learning as to those based upon innateness. Today it is realized that we should not ask the question, "Is this behavior learned or innate?" but rather, "How much of the observed variation in this behavior can be attributed to differences in heredity and how much to differences in experience?"

The most active group studying instinctive behavior today are the ethologists, whose theories have been summarized in Tinbergen's *The Study of Instinct*. It is interesting to consider this book, first because the author makes frequent references to humans, although research in the field is predominantly on birds and fishes, and secondly, because some ethological concepts bear a striking resemblance to Freud's theory of instincts.

A central concept of ethology is that there exist certain patterns of behavior which are released when the proper stimulus is forthcoming. The releaser for fighting in the male stickleback, a small nest-building fish, is any object marked with a red streak like the belly of another male stickleback in the reproductive phase. The releaser for gaping and being fed in young herring gulls is a red patch on the beak of the parents. The fighting and gaping responses can be elicited by a great variety of models bearing little resemblance to the living animal, provided the essential features described above are present. A releaser removes a block which permits a fighting center or a feeding center in the nervous system to operate. Although the anatomical locations of these centers are not specified, a neurophysiological explanation of behavior is implied.

Not all releasers are specific. In the case of a hawk hunting for food, the first level of the instinct (drive) sends the hawk into random searching behavior (appetitive behavior in the ethological terminology). The sight of a woodland will release more specific types of searching behavior adapted to forested areas, and the sight of a small bird will release a direct swooping attack. The captured bird will serve as the releaser of the actions of tearing apart and devouring the prey. Reinforcement learning theory would deal with this sequence of behavior in a very different way, and the problem of innateness versus experience might enter into the interpretation at several places. Observation of animals in nature cannot yield decisive answers since so much of the animal's life history is unknown. But both nature and nurture must play major roles in a hawk's hunting behavior.

This bird is particularly well equipped for seeing movement, and probably has an innate orienting response toward small flying objects. Perhaps the hawk has to learn to swoop down on small birds, but the ability to soar and to swoop depends upon perfect integration of the muscular sensory and nervous systems, and the possible variation of these systems was strictly limited at the fertilized egg stage. And there may be inborn limitations on the type of object which will serve as a goal, "the test of acceptability." It would be very difficult to feed a hawk on grain. Upon this biological foundation is erected a set of behaviors fitted to the specific locality in which the hawk hunts.

Another important ethological concept is *displacement*. If some block exists so that a specific reaction appropriate to a drive is not possible, the energy of the drive may be directed into another channel and displacement activities result. Birds disturbed by a passing airplane may copulate outside of the usual mating season. If energy is dammed up too long it may overflow into any available channel: rats and mice wash and groom when thwarted; birds may preen or hammer at a branch with their bills. Armstrong cites gum-chewing and smoking as modified forms of displacement feeding in man.

Freudian theory also refers to specific energy or *libido* which may be released through normal channels, or dammed up to produce neurotic tension. In a general way, the libido of Freud is identified with the

sex drive, but it includes much more than is implied
in the behavioristic definition of sex (activities leading
to mating). It is difficult to extract from Freud's state-
ments a definite statement regarding the relationship
of libido to drives other than sex, but in his later
writings all sources of pleasure, including even ideas,
came to be considered as manifestations of a sexual
urge. There is a parallel to the concept of releasers
in the Freudian descriptions of psychosexual development. At one time the mother is the releaser for the
libidinal urges of her son resulting in the famous
Oedipus complex. Later on the releaser for these
energies is the sweetheart or the wife, although an
immature person may remain in the infantile state
and be unable to love in an adult fashion. Energy may
be channeled away from its ordinary course. "The
sexual . . . forces," says Freud, "may be sublimated,
that is to say, their energy is turned aside from its
sexual goal and diverted towards other ends, no
longer sexual and socially more valuable. . . . Society
can conceive of no more powerful menace to its culture than would arise from the liberation of sexual
impulses and a return of them to their original goal."
The relationship between the idea of sublimation and
the displacement and overflow reactions of ethology
seems very close.

It is surprising that there are so many parallels
between a theory based upon observations of human
neurotics, and one derived from experiments and observations on birds and fish, but we would go too far
afield if we were to pursue these comparisons further.
Both ethology and psychoanalysis emphasize innate
reaction patterns released by specific stimuli and at-

tribute qualities of physical energy to drives and motives. In contrast, drives in the context of this book are forms of organization of stimulus-response relationships centered in the nervous system. It is hard to see how forms of organization can build up stores of energy, but it is easy to conceive of states of organization which are inherently different in stability. Likewise, difficulty in adaptation might result if different forces were simultaneously operating to produce incompatible forms of organization upon the same nervous system. We will discuss these ideas further as we consider the measurement of motivation, and the problem of conflict.

[VI]

Measuring Motivation

All physical forces can be expressed in terms of three basic dimensions: length, mass, and time. Centimeters, grams, and seconds are the universal units which physicists, chemists, and astronomers employ in their systems of measurement. Energy has many forms—electrical, thermal, kinetic, chemical, and photic—but each can be related quantitatively to any other by means of fundamental equalities based on the centimeter-gram-second system of units. These equalities apply to the behavior of living organisms as well as to planets and hydrogen bombs. We can specify the characteristics of a visual stimulus and of the muscular response it elicits just as accurately as our measuring instruments will permit. Unfortunately, this type of quantification is of limited value in measuring motivation. The nature and energy of responses have no consistent relationship with the nature and energy of the stimuli with which they are associated.

A bell sounding at the end of a school period is the cue for students to become active; five minutes later the same bell ringing for the same length of time is the cue to become quiet. A barely whispered word arouses a violent aggressive assault from a man who has been standing quietly beside a roaring engine. It is not the physics of stimuli, but the instantaneous state of the organism at the time the stimulus energy impinges upon it which determines whether a response will be made, and what it will be. The problem of describing and quantifying these states is the problem of measuring motivation. First, we must decide what we are to measure, then we must try to devise units and methods.

Fundamentally, the problem is one of measuring organization rather than force, and the centimeter-gram-second system of quantification is not suitable for our purposes. Theorists who conceive of motivation and drives as sources of energy, as springs which wind themselves tighter and tighter until the stored energy flows into a response system, should be obligated to account for the energy in physical terms. But, in fact, most such theorists employ the term energy in a non-quantitative and even nonmaterial sense, a practice which is disturbing to individuals familiar with common scientific usage. Shifting the measurement of motivation from the domain of energy to that of organization is an advance, but many problems remain.

It is easy to see that a crystal is more organized than a liquid, a symphony orchestra more than a group of musicians gathered from hither and yon. Clearly the most useful indices of the organization of an orchestra are some characteristics of the music which it produces. But not every characteristic is a suitable measure of organization, and one would not judge an orchestra by its sound output in decibels, nor the time in seconds taken to complete Beethoven's Fifth Symphony. Yet force and speed measures have been

favorite devices of experimenters seeking to quantify
motivation. It is more logical, though technically more
difficult, to base a criterion of organization upon the
degree to which individuals constituting a group work
toward a common goal. In the orchestra this means
that all the players follow the conductor's baton rather
than their personal interpretation of a composition.
As applied to the behavior of an individual, the integration is predominantly across time units, and motivation can be considered as an attribute of the temporal
organization of behavior patterns. Strong motivation
is characterized by consistency of direction and by
resistance to diversion. Such a definition offers promise
as the basis for measuring motivation quantitatively.

Whatever characteristics of responses are chosen as
indicators of strength of motivation should yield consistent results when the same individual is measured
under the same conditions. If test 1 shows that rat A
has stronger hunger drive than rat B after twenty-four
hours of food deprivation, test 2 which purports to
measure this drive should also rank rat A higher in
hunger. The point may be illustrated by reference to
two distinct methods of measuring temperature. In
the ordinary household thermometer, temperature is
estimated as a function of the volume of a fluid en-
closed in a glass bulb. Every thermometer is calibrated
at a standard temperature so that readings can be compared from time to time and from place to place.
Even if there were no calibrations, it would be possible to determine whether one glass of water were
warmer than another, if the same thermometer were
used for both. Careful measurements with a ruler
would suffice for this purpose. A second method of
measuring temperature is based upon the voltage gen-

erated when two dissimilar metals are placed in contact. It is known that this voltage varies with temperature, and devices based upon this principle are known as thermocouples. If we have a way to measure voltage, we can determine temperature differences, though calibration will be necessary if we are to use the standard Fahrenheit or centigrade scales. The point is that even without determination of a zero point we can be sure that if glass A is warmer than glass B on the thermometer, it will also be found warmer on the thermocouple. We can ask no less of the "thermometers" we use to measure drives and motives.

Various methods have been employed in attempts to measure the strength of motivation. Rate or amount of response, effort put forth in overcoming obstructions, and choice between goal objects have all been employed. The studies by Warden and his collaborators on the Columbia obstruction apparatus are well known. Albino rats were at different times deprived of food or water, separated from animals of the opposite sex, and in the case of females, separated from their young litters. In order to reach the goal appropriate to each condition of deprivation, the animals were forced to cross an electrically charged grid. Motivation was measured in terms of the number of crossings per test period when a standard charge was applied to the grid. Undoubtedly the electric shock produced an acquired fear drive, making the grid more than a simple barrier, and generating an approach-avoidance conflict.

The results following food deprivation may be cited as typical. Hunger drive in male white rats, as measured by number of crossings, was at a low point immediately after feeding, increased to a maximum after up to four days of deprivation, and then decreased. In females, the maximum was reached after one day, and the decline began on the second day. Delaying the presentation of food after crossing the grid greatly weakened grid-crossing response.

When different types of drives, each at its maximum strength, were compared the order from strongest to weakest was: maternal (in females), thirst, hunger, sex (males and females), and exploratory (only males tested). The incentive for exploration was a system of alleys fitted with various objects which had been found interesting to rats.

Conclusions on the relative strength of different types of motivation are justifiable only insofar as the measuring devices employed are actually valid indicators of the central process we are trying to quantify. The obstruction method yields reliable results from test to test, but this does not tell us whether different methods would yield similar results. An extensive comparison of several methods of measuring drive was made by Anderson, who employed forty-seven measures of drive strength and learning in one study, and supplemented this by a comparison of four emotional measures with tests of sex and exploratory drive. Each test was administered as a series of subtests, and reliability was found to be high. Multiple measures were taken as follows: exploratory drive (7 tests), thirst drive (10 tests), hunger drive (14 tests), sex drive (7 tests), and learning (6 tests). Correlations between different supposed criteria of the hunger and thirst drives were not significant, but there were some significant intercorrelations between different "measures" of exploratory and sex drives. Even here an individual which did well on one test might do poorly on a test which had been expected to measure the same quality. Anderson conjectured that better agreement between the separate measures of sex and exploratory drives were due to the greater dependence of these drives upon external factors, which were more comparable from subject to subject than the physiological changes produced by food and water deprivation.

Most of the tests which Anderson used were measures of energy such as speed of running, time spent in digging through sand to reach a goal, or number of crossings of a charged grid. It is impossible to account for the discrepancy between different measures of the same drive if the energy component of behavior is dependent upon a state of drive which is in turn dependent upon the degree of deprivation. But if the energy component is partially dependent upon exogenous stimuli, perhaps the same exogenous stimuli which direct activity, one would not expect equal output in two different test situations simply because the internal state of the organism (say its water content or blood sugar level) was the same. Thus, it is doubtful that consistent measures of motivation can be based upon the energy and speed of a series of responses. Perhaps the animal which takes longest to tunnel through a sand barrier to get a drink of water is really the best motivated because he persists longer without reinforcement.

The failure to obtain significant intercorrelations between supposed measures of the same drive is not the only basis for concluding that response measures based upon energy are not accurate indicators of the factors motivating behavior. Studies on rats made grossly obese by overeating after destruction of a small area in the hypothalamus have shown that the surgically treated subjects actually will not work as hard for food nor tolerate as much bitter additive as will normal rats. Similar results have been obtained with genetically obese mice. Measuring hunger drive by the quantity of food eaten leads to the conclusion when quinine is added to the regular diet that drive is greater in normal mice; when fat is added obese mice eat more; and consumption by each kind of mouse is essentially equal on the regular diet. Even in the lowly mouse, motivation is based largely upon the nature of incentives.

A further difficulty in attempting to measure motivation in terms of energy is encountered when we try to evaluate "freezing behavior" in a frightened animal or person. Strong motivation may result in less rather than more movement.

Since the energy expended in a response is not a satisfactory index of motivation, we now consider directional measures. Every segment of behavior, if observed over a sufficiently long period of time, can be completely described in terms of its direction and energy. The requirement that observations must continue for a considerable period is necessary for an observer to distinguish between random changes of direction, and directional tendencies which are maintained long enough to be referred to a specific goal. Now it is obvious that behavior cannot have energy without direction, nor direction without energy. To be sure, the direction may change so frequently that the observer cannot detect any consistent pattern or goal orientation, though energy output (as in convulsions) may be high. There may be also wishes or aspirations (directions) which do not result in behavior (energy), but these are inaccessible to scientific analysis. Now if we reject energy measures as indices of motivation, we must adopt some directional measure or discard the concept. In fact the argument might seem to be leading to a rejection since we have been arguing against the directive properties of drive states, and would even partially agree with Brown, who says, "Every case of directed behavior is to be ascribed, not to drives or motives, but to the capacity of stimulus cues, whether innate or acquired to elicit reactions." This statement, however, somewhat arbitrarily separates directional and energetic properties of response on the basis of their dependence upon stimulus cues.

The thing to remember is that the same cues which direct behavior may also have (perhaps always have) activating and facilitating functions. The reverse is not true. There are activating and facilitating forces which are not cues, and these can have motivational effects without directive ones. Drives and motives are not behavior, but labels which we apply to states of organization in the nervous system. We say that motivation is strong in an organism which maintains orientation to a single cue or class of cues over a prolonged period of time. This means that instantaneous determinations of orientation have no motivational significance; the period of observation must be long enough to clearly detect departures from random (non-goal-directed) activity. The motive state in general is associated with stability of organization toward a goal. Only to the extent that stability is determined by factors which are not cues can Brown's dictum apply. It is more applicable to drives related to blood chemistry than to the appetites and expressive drives.

The importance of the period of observation in motivational research must be emphasized. In the first place, a whole hierarchy of motivations emerges as we alter the length of the time unit of observation. Over the period of a day it is easy to find activities motivated by thirst, hunger, sex, fear, sleepiness, and the expressive drives. These are functions which interest biologists and many physiologically oriented psychologists, and the behavior patterns involved are often relatable to primary needs of the body. If we had only one twenty-four-hour sample of any one person's behavior available for examination we could deduce little about his motivation regarding education, marriage, wealth, power, or artistic and scientific creation. Of course, observation may be supplemented by direct inquiry, securing the opinions of other persons, and by the study of life history data. However, in regard to long-term directions, any one day's behavior may be completely nonrepresentative. An extended acquaintance with the regularly recurrent patterns of an individual's behavior is essential to understanding his long-term motivation. The very language we use in describing motivation is dependent upon whether we are dealing with directional trends over minutes, hours, days, weeks, or years.

Difference in time scales affects more than the matter of measuring motivation. It is involved in the argument regarding the extent to which human motivation has been emancipated from dependence upon primary and acquired drives based upon biological needs. Biology is not suspended while the novelist writes a book, the physician acquires an education, or the revolutionary plans the overthrow of the government, but this is not evidence that the long-period stable direction of their behavior is due to the same primary drives which insure their attention to bodily requirements. The persistence of the novelist, and the others cited, is toward a goal which has no real existence while it is serving as an incentive. This particularly human characteristic does not mean that the future is affecting the present, but rather that the past affects the reinforcing value of partial achievement in the present.

Returning to problems of measurement, we may consider whether the concept of motivation as stabilized organization of directed behavior leads to useful and valid techniques of quantification. Such techniques might be of two types: (1) noting the resistance of behavior to change of direction by distracting stimuli or physiological changes, and (2) observing the acquisition and persistence of goal-oriented behavior in the absence of reinforcement. Studies on conflict and on performance decrement caused by fatigue would come under class (1). Experiments on frustration, and possibly latent learning experiments, would be included under class (2). In a frustrating situation strong motivation may be expressed either in resistance of an old habit to extinction, or in ready acquisition of a new habit directed toward the same goal. By selecting goals appropriate to different time scales, analogous measures are possible both on short-period and long-period forms of motivation.

In Diagram 12 an attempt has been made to schematize the concept of the hierarchical system of motivation based upon differences in time-scale. Each of the shortest sections is intended to represent a sequence

DIAGRAM 12

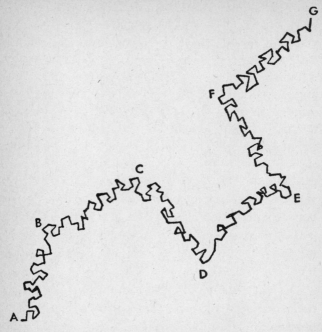

of action directed toward a particular incentive. There
are also six longer sequences somewhat vaguely separated if one looks only at the junction points
(B, C, D, E, F), but clearly distinguished when one
looks at the whole pattern. Finally a trend from lower
left to upper right (A to G) is evident. If there were
neither middle-period nor long-period trends, the short-
period oscillations would balance in such a way that
the line would never stray far from A. Physiological
psychologists and biologists have dealt mainly with
short-period motivation. The longer trends are less
amenable to experimentation, but are of interest to developmental psychologists, students of personality and
psychiatrists.

It appears impossible to specify one best criterion
for each motive, or one general criterion which will
serve as a basis for comparing different motives. Motivation involves many interactions between physiological conditions of the organism and the perceived surroundings. Presumably the common meeting place
and integrating center for these determinants lies
somewhere in the central nervous system. But the factors are so numerous, and the relations between each
so complex that a general equation defining them
seems out of reach for the present. Conceivably the
rate of acquiring a new response under different motivational states might provide a basis of comparison
between say hunger, sex, and exploratory drives, but
it is by no means certain that the most efficient motive
for one response would be most efficient for all learning.

This does not mean that useful scales of motivational strength covering local areas of interest are
impossible. In any one experiment we may vary deprivation time, heredity, previous training, hormone
content of the blood, and observe the effect on some
measure of the directiveness of responses toward particular cues and incentives. If, as is likely, the results
vary as the incentive varies, and there are inconsist-
encies between different measures of persistence, there
need be no cause for alarm. This would be expected
if motivation depends upon a state of organization
which fluctuates with the ebb and flow of multiple
forces. The facts are bothersome only if the experimenter feels bound to consider motivation as all drive,
drive as all energy, and cues simply as agents which
open the valves and release the energy.

[VII]

The Physiology
of Motivation

I HAVE an old volume on physiology which contains an illustration of the brain. On the figure the artist has labeled centers for intellect, character, interests, and personality attributes. Presumably, activity in specific areas of the brain was supposed to provide motivation for specific kinds of action. Today we know that this is not the way functions are localized in the brain. In fact, the nervous system participates as a whole in many activities. Memory in rats and monkeys, for example, is affected more by the amount of cerebral cortex removed than by the particular areas removed. On the other hand, there is an increasing amount of data showing that emotional and motivational aspects of behavior can be modified by events occurring in specific regions of the brain. This does not mean that motivation is solely located in these centers, but rather that they are of critical importance in a larger system.

The importance of the hypothalamus as the integrative center for eating, activity, temperature regulation, sexual responses, and the general visceral changes characteristic of strong emotional arousal has been amply demonstrated. In some instances, two antagonistic centers which operate in dynamic balance have been found. Despite the dramatic effects which follow stimulation or extirpation of these centers, they are probably not essential to motivated behavior. In the section on hunger drive it was stated that rats with a particular hypothalamic lesion starve to death in the midst of food. This is true if ordinary laboratory diets only are available, but noneating animals can be tempted by particularly delicious tidbits, and gradually brought back to practically normal eating behavior. Another group of brain structures important for emotional behavior are collectively known as the rhinencephalon. These are the old (in an evolutionary sense) portions of the cerebrum, and are much the same throughout the vertebrate kingdom. Removal of one portion, the amygdala, produces an unusually docile, unemotional animal. Such a specimen goes through his paces, but it is very hard to teach him new habits. No function is wholly lost, but the thresholds for fear, rage, and pleasure appear to be raised. Other sections of the rhinencephalon seem to play a critical part in arousal and maintenance of emotions.

Still another portion of the nervous system which is important in the physiology of motivation is the diffuse network of fibers known as the reticular formation which has been studied by Magoun and his collaborators. The system fed by afferent neurons from all sense organs has an activating function—regulation of the general level of vigilance rather than control of specific responses.

A famous experiment by Olds and Milner showed that rats can learn to press a bar, and maintain the habit for prolonged periods when "rewarded" by electrical stimulation of local brain areas. Local stimulation was obtained by aseptically inserting fine wires through a hole drilled in the skull. Each bar press operated a switch which sent a pulse of current into the brain. When the current was disconnected from the switch the rats stopped pressing the bar. This technique is now a standard procedure, and rates of learning and of extinguishing the reinforced response are similar to that obtained when food or water rewards are used. Interestingly, the brain regions where stimulation has been proved to be rewarding are parts of the old rhinencephalon. These experiments have led to a physiological theory of pleasure, and a new basis for hedonistic theories in psychology.

Motivation in behavioral terms implies the maintenance of a disposition to respond in a particular direction until reinforcement occurs. Neurophysiologically, this involves both activation and selective facilitation and inhibition. If reward involves activation of particular brain areas as the Olds and Milner study suggests, there must be some explanation of why eating in one instance, drinking in another, and listening to an orchestra in yet another, will sometimes activate these areas and sometimes not. Directing or motivating behavior becomes then a matter of determining the stimuli which have reinforcing properties. As one possible mechanism hypothalamic centers may facilitate or inhibit the rewarding properties of stimuli associated with internal drive states. Activity in the brain regions concerned with emotional patterns could modify the reinforcing power of the stimuli which elicit acquired drives.

The foregoing discussion of the physiology of motivation has skirted the subject of the relation of motives to needs, and has concentrated on the nervous system, particularly the brain. This does not mean that motives are divorced from the rest of the body, any more than the brain exists independently of the other organ systems. Needs of the organism influence the brain through afferent nerve impulses, and through modification of the physical and chemical properties of the blood which bathes the brain cells. These influences from the periphery are important to motivational physiology, it is true, but the basic physiological problems of behavioral organization lie in the central nervous system. Neurophysiologists are just beginning to work on the problem of how the brain interprets the signals which it receives.

Drive states which are related to peripheral processes do provide explanations of why a particular type of behavior ceases. Drinking restores water content of the body, and eating elevates the blood sugar level. To be sure, a thirsty dog will drink until he has made up his water deficit, and then stop, although the water is still in his stomach and cannot have yet affected tissue needs. Such occurrences teach us that nerve impulses arising from the stomach probably provide information in addition to that derived from the concentration of the blood.

Motivation based upon acquired drives also wears thin, although need and satiation cannot be identified in the physical terms used for hunger and thirst. We remark on the intense activity of the dedicated musician, but the most devoted artist can go stale. He breaks up his practice by recreation, by attention to his biological needs, by sleep, and even then he may complain of "mental fatigue." "Mental" because he is not muscularly exhausted, but tired of making and listening to his own music. Stimulus novelty seems to be essential, particularly for the maintenance of motivational states not supported by strong internal drives. The relationship of new perceptual content to motivation has been thoroughly discussed by Hebb in *The Organization of Behavior*. What is perceived as novel depends upon the extent of generalization and discrimination of stimulus characteristics. The music critic is trained to compare two performances of the same composition by different conductors. Novelty for such a trained person is provided by the discrimination of fine differences between stimuli which would not be perceived by a novice or by a child. In a sense, there is a chain reaction set up by the interaction of discrimination learning and motivation. Each stage of learning increases the potentiality for recognition of novelty which can then motivate additional learning.

In summary we present the following working hypothesis for the relationship between motivation and stimulus novelty. Motivation requires that the nervous system be both activated and organized. Excessive novelty may activate without organizing a directed response. Repetition of a stimulus produces habituation, in other words, a decrease of activation. What is new depends upon the organism as well as upon the physical characteristics of the stimulus. The greater the ability to discriminate, the more novelty the world contains. The greater the ability to generalize, the less apt is any situation to be completely new, for elements common to previous experience will always be found.

Motivation thus is the psychological consequence of a balanced state of the nervous system. Chemical factors bias the sensitivity of the system, their effects being most clearly shown in the hypothalamic nuclei. Into this information processing system come streams of nerve impulses from internal receptors and from distance receptors (ears, eyes, and nose). Most, if not all of this input has a dual role: nonspecific activation which lowers response thresholds, and organization of specific patterns. Motivational state is a neural rather than a humoral phenomenon, though hormones, glucose, carbon dioxide, and perhaps other substances modulate neural reactivity.

Motivation can be terminated by biochemical events which raise the activation threshold, or by the production of a refractory condition in some part of the neural system which maintains the organized pattern. Both processes may occur simultaneously and their respective importance is dependent upon the nature of the drive state. At one extreme is behavior motivated by asphyxiation, which terminates when oxygen and carbon dioxide balance are restored; at the other is exploratory behavior, which has not been tied to any chemical deficit. Yet it seems reasonable to postulate some common physiological feature of both which leads to directed and coördinated behavior.

[VIII]

Motivational Conflict

EVERYONE IS FAMILIAR with the fable of the donkey who was placed midway between two piles of hay, and starved to death because he could not decide which he should eat. Psychologically the story is unsound, for in this particular type of conflict it is not difficult to resolve the conflicting response tendencies or motivations if one assumes a gradient of motivational strength dependent upon distance from the incentive. The donkey in the fable is placed in an approach-approach conflict, but the slightest move to go to one haystack will strengthen one motivation, and weaken the tendency to approach the other pile. It may take some time for an imbalance to develop, but a permanent state of equality of two approach motivations is impossible.

Another kind of motivational conflict is expressed in the phrase, "between the devil and the deep blue sea." In contrast with approach-approach, an avoidance-avoidance conflict is not self-resolving. Approaching the devil increases fear, and the individual retreats toward the sea. But the sea becomes more terrifying as one gets closer to it, and so back to the devil. Thus the organism oscillates back and forth between the two unpleasant choices. Resolution of such a conflict, of course, comes only if it turns out that the devil isn't real, and that his mask is funny rather than fearful. In other words, the significance of the cues themselves must be altered.

A third type of conflict involves a single stimulus (or different stimuli which lie very close to each other) which evokes motivation for both avoidance and approach. As the organism, motivated in a positive manner, approaches, it is more strongly motivated to retreat. Resolution of such a conflict may be very difficult if two strong motivational states are involved. Richter has found that rats which have recovered from a dose of poison ingested with food will sometimes starve to death when offered regular food, presumably through fear of poisoning. Hunger increases with food deprivation for a time and then declines. If, at its maximum, hunger is not strong enough to overcome the fear based upon the poisoning episode, there is little chance that the subject will resume eating spontaneously thereafter.

Motivational conflict is perhaps the main theme of abnormal psychology. The coexistence of incompatible response tendencies results in vacillation, indecision, and excessive production of nonadaptive behavior, false starts, mannerisms, excessive vocalization, or visceral disturbances. The language used to describe conflict may be that of Freud, and expressed in terms of id, ego, and superego. Alternatively, the language of stimulus-response psychology or that of the ethologists may be employed. All students of behavior recognize the existence of the problem.

It is impossible here to deal adequately with the problems of conflict. All that can be done is to list some thoughts regarding biological aspects of the subject. Most innate needs of organisms are met by going out into the world and locating something which will satisfy the need. The conflicts which arise from coexisting biological needs are of an approach-approach variety, and are self-resolving under ordinary circumstances, though it is possible to set up situations in which selecting one goal eliminates the possibility of reaching the other. A man may have enough money to buy a coat to keep him warm or food for a week, but not both. Such conflicts involve more than the comparison of two possible responses. The man must have learned something about the value of money to know that making one choice rules out the other, and he must fear the consequences of not having food or not having an overcoat. Such conflicts are not possible in rats or monkeys.

The non-spontaneously-resolving type conflicts always involve a tendency to avoid. Behind such avoidance is the state of the organism we designate as fearful. Fear, elicited by pain, by conditioning, or by unfamiliar and incongruous perceptions, is a pervasive emotional state in serious conflict situations. Fear is disorganizing because it represents the actions of forces leading to responses which are incompatible with other motivational states. Resolution of conflict must then depend upon the reduction of fear in relation to the strength of other motives. In the case of motives which include a strong internal component, for example hunger, powerful facilitation of approach behavior may be provided by such factors as blood sugar level or hunger contractions. The expressive drives fare less well in such conflicts since they must compete with fear without aid from sex hormones, tissue dehydration, or lowered blood sugar concentration.

Conflicts may be resolved and stable motivational organization attained by reducing fear. This is not always easy. Fear is astoundingly persistent, but it is vulnerable to certain agents which leave other behavior essentially intact. For example, having produced a conflict in cats by subjecting them to an air blast when they approached their food, Masserman found that alcohol reduced their fear more than their hunger. He thus produced an apparent resolution of the conflicts. (Unfortunately half of the "neurotic" cats became confirmed alcoholics as a result of this pharmacological therapy.) Currently there is great interest in a class of drugs known as tranquilizers which reduce fear without serious impairment of approach-motivated behavior. Frontal lobotomy disconnects the frontal portion of the cerebrum from the rest of the brain. Used on patients with intractable pain, it gives great relief, not from the pain itself but from the anxiety associated with it.

Pharmacology and neurosurgery are rather drastic means of reducing fear and are not free of side effects. Avoidance responses may be extinguished, as may other responses, if they are not reinforced. The problem here is to bring the drive state out into the open. Keeping a safe distance from an imitation devil gives no opportunity to learn that it really isn't dangerous. Avoiding such a devil is adjustive in that it reduces drive strength by anticipating the fear which would be manifest in proximity, but adjustment is purchased at the cost of activity based on the "expressive drives." The problem of distinguishing a real devil from an imaginary one is a task for education, and for psychotherapy if education is not adequate. Fortunately our ancestors discovered some of the ways of making this distinction, and the child learns much of this from his parents. But ancestors are not infallible, and some of the devils which appeared real to them are rather pale imitations to us though we are not always quite sure. Furthermore, our forebears could scarcely be expected to foresee the implications of new scientific discoveries and new forms of social organization. The point is that some tension and conflict appear to be inevitable accompaniments of an evolving society, and that the testing of devils to determine whether they are real or not may be a dangerous but socially necessary enterprise. We do not know whether man, like other species, will reach a stable universal type of social organization. If the present state of social flux proves to be a temporary phase of human history, motivational conflicts may be greatly reduced sometime in the future.

[IX]

Human Motivation

IN LABORATORY EXPERIMENTS on motivation, an attempt is made to keep all except one or two factors constant in order to appraise the effects of the variables chosen for study. Much more complex are the motivations behind the behavior of men and women in everyday life. What, for example, are the motivations which keep a scientist occupied with a career of scientific research? At the end of each month he receives a token reward (pay check in nonpsychological terms) which is convertible into food, clothing, and housing to care for his biological requirements. With this token he also contributes to the maintenance of a wife and family. He does not believe in the existence of either conjugal or paternal instincts, therefore he must attribute his motivation to the rewards of family living. Even if inherited income made it possible for him to acquire all his and his family's needs without working for them, he would still have some occupation. Like other men in the United States, he is supposed to justify his existence by at least going through the motions of being usefully employed. Put another way, he eats to work as much as he works to eat.

He also has motivation intrinsic to scientific activity

itself. Manipulating new equipment and observing new phenomena provide strong rewards, particularly at the start of a new project. As novelty wears off, these motives may not suffice to carry the project through to completion. Fear of not meeting the deadline for a report, or of not receiving promotion can help provide the persistence of effort needed to complete a study. Occasionally, motivation based upon competition with another scientist working in the same field may be operative—extra credit generally goes to the first man to announce a new discovery. Then there are various forms of recognition for research accomplishment given by the scientific fraternity ranging from applause for a paper presented at a meeting to the Nobel prize. Which of these factors motivates our scientist? All of them do at one time or another, and most of them are in operation all the time.

When different motivating forces work together in the same direction, it is impossible to parcel out the total motivation percentagewise to each of the contributing factors. For our purposes, fortunately, this is not an important question. We are interested in the problem of the degree to which the biological principles which we have been considering will furnish a broad explanatory base for interpretation of the behavior of any human being. Can we meet the challenge of D. K. Adams' question, "What . . . are the tissue needs that supply the energy for our efforts toward assertion, aggression, mink coats, and status?" (1954). Adams replies that the connections are so remote, if indeed they exist, that for the present we had better restrict ourselves to psychological constructs rather than employ neurophysiological models.

Before trying to answer Adams' question, however, we must rephrase portions of it. A biological perspective on motivation includes tissue needs, but is by no means synonymous with them. Needs cannot explain behavior, though behavior must somehow be geared to meet them. Nor can needs supply energy. This is produced by the oxidation of foodstuffs. Our strivings for assertion, aggression, mink coats, and status must be described in terms of behavioral organization rather than motor energy. The best way to maintain status in some situations is to be passive, and the energy of a nasty remark need be no greater than that of a friendly word. Yet the motivations are very different. The question we shall try to answer is: "How much of the variability in human motivation can be explained in biological terms?"

Our answer, "A considerable part," has two important qualifications. (1) Acceptance of the answer is based upon faith in the unity of natural phenomena, rather than upon a complete physiological explanation of the motivation of every human act. Some general propositions will be presented, but a complete biological model is definitely in the unforeseeable future. (2) The usefulness of purely psychological constructs without regard to neurophysiological underpinning is not denied. Similar situations occur in other sciences. The neurophysiologist believes that the phenomena he observes are the result of chemical and physical processes at the cellular level, but in much of his work he is content to use such physiological terms as excitation and inhibition. There are occasions, however, when he profits from using physiochemical concepts based upon molecules rather than neurones. This is essential,

for example, when he attempts to explain the neurological effects of drugs.

What are the biological principles by which we
shall attempt to explain human motivation? First, we
have the so-called primary drives associated with biological needs. We have cited evidence that the humoral agents (hormones, blood constituents) are much
less important as regulators of human behavior than
they are in lower mammals. Stimuli resulting from
visceral distension and contraction are also associated
with needs and primary drives, and these are much
the same in man and animals. There is universal recognition of the importance of humoral and visceral
factors in the metabolic processes of men, but they
don't seem to go far enough in explaining the differences in motivation between men and rats. Rats and
men both learn to go to food, but rats don't seek mink
coats or write scientific treatises. Neither do men
when they are confined in a concentration camp on a
subminimal diet. The primary drives can still preempt
the center of the motivational stage under extreme
conditions.

A second important construct is that of acquired
drive, which we have identified with emotional arousal.
These states also have physiological correlates, but
they originate as conditioned responses to cues rather
than as aspects of tissue need. The ultimate dependence of acquired drives upon reinforcement of primary drives is frequently assumed, but under favorable conditions well-established emotional responses
persist for long periods in the absence of primary
reinforcement. We have chosen to consider pleasurable excitement as a drive, rather than as reinforce-

ment, and have placed upon it the burden of maintaining various ingestive and erotic appetites.

Finally, we have placed great emphasis on the importance of perceived novelty as a basis of motivation. It is hard to locate a physiological basis for "expressive drives," though speculation is certainly in order and testable hypotheses are being proposed. Regardless of physiology, the behavioral consequences of novelty are a matter of observation. Becoming familiar with a stimulus decreases its activating power and motivation declines. However, organisms do not simply wait around passively to be activated by stimuli which happen along. Behavior tends to follow lines which will provide organizing stimuli. Rats, dogs, and people explore their environment. In man, daydreaming and hallucinations regularly occur when a monotonous environment fails to provide sufficient sensory input. Ennui (mild activation without organization) is in fact just short of pain as a negative reinforcing agent. Learning (the strengthening of stimulus-response connections) is the result of reducing the degree of activation by familiarization with the new elements of a stimulus.

This concept of expressive drives carries within it the possibility of tremendously extending the motivating power of cues without regard to their effects on tissue requirements. An individual who has learned how to discriminate finds elements of novelty which were not apparent before the discrimination learning took place. We are not speaking here of learning of a particular discrimination, but of learning how to discriminate in a general area. Part of the motivation of the expert comes from the fact that he can intellectually explore his field of competence, finding new items to activate patterns of neuronal activity where the novice is simply confused. Frequently getting deeply into a subject, even one far removed from immediate rewards, provides motivation for continued learning. Perhaps such "ego-involvement" is simply a by-product of the change of the activation potential of stimuli which follows from learning to discriminate them from closely related stimuli.

The argument above is frankly a bit of armchair deduction, but it seems to do no violence either to psychological or physiological principles. However, the critic may wonder how motivation for learning how to discriminate originated in the first place, and what basis there is for assuming that discriminative behavior can be reinforcing in its own right. The answer to these questions must rest upon a consideration of the development of motivation within the individual.

Most of the chemical and nervous mechanisms for facilitating and activating the central nervous system are present in the infant. At first, the mode of activation makes little difference in the behavior of the child. He kicks and cries in much the same manner when he is hungry, or colicky. Gradually some activating stimuli also acquire specific organizing properties, and behavior appropriate to each situation is learned. Some activators and sensitizers never can acquire organizing properties, because of their diffuse effects on the nervous system. Lowered blood sugar may make one irritable or faint, but so can several drugs. We are not equipped to discriminate the chemical nature of substances entering brain cells, and hence no organization of specific response patterns can occur. Hunger pangs are different, since they can be differentiated from discomfort from other sources, and can participate both in activation and organization.

The infant comes in contact with many objects and learns to discriminate these in terms of their relationship to the reduction of activation to an optimal level. Objects become important in two ways: as cues which organize responses, and as activators of the central nervous system. In both extremes of activation (deep sleep and convulsive frenzy) organization is at a minimum. In psychological terms, the activation process is an emotional response, which is disorganizing if it is excessive and motivating if sufficiently limited. Limited activation combined with organization is "pleasurable," and operates to motivate approach to the stimuli which elicited the pleasure. This leads to consummatory activity and decreased activation. Excessive activation is "painful" and can be reduced by avoiding the activating cues. Note that this model gives an explanation for the attractiveness of close approaches to danger, riding on roller coasters, looking at waterfalls, watching prize fights. At a safe distance, activation and organization proceed only to the "pleasure" point. A closer contact would be emotionally disorganizing.

Among the objects to which the infant learns to respond are other people. In his helpless state all his nutritive rewards, all relief from discomfort is associated with the ministrations of an adult human. Evidence is strong that lack of loving care during early periods of life has long-lasting effects on the ability of the adolescent and adult to make social adjustments. There is another way in which the child develops important relationships with adults. He finds that he can solve many of his problems and be rewarded most readily by imitating the actions of others. At first he imitates his parents and siblings. Later his choice of models is greatly extended, and upon his selection and the adequacy of his imitation depends his ultimate role in his community. This idea has been thoroughly developed by Miller and Dollard who describe many features of contemporary society which reward imitation. Some forces, of course, operate to discourage and limit the process.

The combination of imitation with the expressive drives of exploration and manipulation is perhaps the most important source of particularly human behavior. The model leads the imitator to the objects to be discriminated, and rewards the first successful discriminations. In the absence of interfering factors, the process of learning a discrimination organizes the nervous system so that it is more readily activated than before in similar situations.

The developmental sequence presented here is a progression from motivation largely determined by biological drives to motivation based largely upon the element of perceived novelty. This more advanced type of motivation does not replace but supplements the drives based upon needs and upon emotional arousal. Its full development, in fact, is based upon learning which is motivated by the earlier appearing mechanisms. This point of view is similar to that expressed by Hunt (1960) who, without abandoning classical drive reduction theory, finds it necessary to include other types of motivation (our expressive or information seeking drives) in any explanation of child development.

Granted that needs operating indirectly through internal drive states are important in establishing second and third order motivational systems, does the maintenance of these systems depend upon occasional reinforcement by food, drink, orgasm, or relief from pain? Our concept of reward in terms of neurological organization rather than tissue need certainly allows for the possibility that functional independence might be attained. However, the stimuli associated with tissue deprivation retain strong activating and organizing properties, stronger ordinarily than any others. There is ample justification for speaking of these states as preemptive drives. In a well-developed technological society, however, such drives do not conflict with the expressive motives, but alternate with them in orderly fashion. If our hunch is right, acquired motivation is probably autonomous, though never exempt from replacement by other learned responses. The activating power of stimuli, though not necessarily their organizing powers, are quite stable unless training is directed at restructuring the emotional responses (activation level).

Our remarks on the sufficiency of biological principles to explain human motivation have followed a middle course. Need has been given a prominent place in the development of motives, but only by its indirect action upon the nervous system. The long-term motivations and aspirations of the adult are regarded as potentially independent of biological need except as they happen to be incompatible with short-term drive and appetite-motivated behavior. The neurological model of motivation has dealt with two concepts, activation and organization. The definition of these concepts has purposely been kept very general because scientific knowledge in this area is still undeveloped and theories are in flux.

One serious problem which any biological theory of motivation must face is the explanation of maladaptive behavior. How are motives acquired which result in behavior inimical to the welfare of the behavior? Another book would be required to deal adequately with this question. By divorcing the meaning of "reinforcement" from "need fulfillment," and making lowered activation rather than reward the essential for learning, it is possible to explain acquisition and retention of maladaptive behavior within a physiological framework. There is no necessity of invoking a Freudian death wish, nor postulating learning mechanisms which are unique for neurotics.

Another human trait which must be fitted into a biological scheme is that of altruism. Our common sense tells us that the man who risks his life to save a child from drowning, the nun who renounces marriage and material comfort in order to serve in a hospital, the volunteer who submits to an untested and possibly dangerous medical procedure, that these people are not behaving neurotically although the outcome of their actions may be biologically maladaptive for them personally. The motivation for altruistic behavior is undoubtedly complex, but reinforcement theory can handle the situation if reinforcement is made a matter of neurophysiology rather than satisfaction of tissue need.

In a sense, then, man is motivationally no more complex than his mammalian relatives. They, too, learn to behave so as to satisfy their needs. They, too, develop food preferences based upon taste and texture rather than nutritive value. Fear, rage, and pleasurable excitement are in the behavioral repertory of chimpanzee and dog; fear in that of the rat. Exploratory and manipulatory motivation has been amply demonstrated in many animals. The quest for social status which assures priority in competitive situations is reflected in the dominance structure of social mammals and birds as well as in man. Differences lie in the immensely greater human capacity for discrimination, and in the lessened dependence upon the presence of objective cues. Language gives man an opportunity to extend the variety and number of stimuli far beyond any subhuman, and in particular to establish a whole hierarchy of goals within goals. The student studies to pass an examination, to pass a course, to obtain a degree, to get a job, to achieve community status, to be a well-integrated person. The new dimension in human motivation is time-binding, the establishment of superordinate goals which encompass but do not conflict with subgoals. The stability of this superstructure is based in physiology as well as in learning. Witness the effects of an overactive thyroid gland, a tumor on the brain, a few ounces of alcohol.

When we deal with individuals we must consider motivational problems from a psychobiological viewpoint. Motivation is not a thing, but a state of organization, and the higher levels of organization interact with the lower. It has been said that the next era in psychology will see the same attention paid to problems of motivation that the last half-century gave to learning. Biology and psychology must combine forces for the effort.

Bibliography

FURTHER EXCURSIONS into the field of motivation might well start with some of the papers and books listed below. Special mention should also be made of the series, *Nebraska Symposium on Motivation*, which has appeared annually since 1953. Books on the list were selected to present diversified viewpoints on subjects treated in this book. A few research papers are cited because their results are referred to directly in the text. No attempt has been made to give credit for every idea borrowed by the author, but he acknowledges in particular the contributions of D. O. Hebb and N. E. Miller, whose views have been influential in the development of this book.

Adams, D. K. *The anatomy of personality.* Studies in Psychol., New York, Random House, 1954.

Allee, W. C. *Cooperation among animals: with human implications.* Rev. ed. New York, Schuman, 1951.

Anderson, E. E. The interrelationships of drives in the male albino rat. *Comp. Psychol. Monog. 14* (6):1-119, 1938.

Andersson, B. The effect of injections of hypertonic NaCl-solutions into different parts of the hypothalamus of goats. *Acta Physiol. Scand. 28*:188-201, 1953.

Armstrong, E. A. The nature and function of displacement activities. In *Physiological mechanisms in animal behavior.* New York, Academic Press, 1950.

Ax, A. F. The physiological differentiation between fear and anger in humans. *Psychosomatic Med.* 15:433-442, 1953.

Beach, F. A. A review of physiological and psychological studies of sexual behavior in mammals. *Physiol. Rev.* 27:240-307, 1947.

Beebe-Center, J. G. Feeling and emotion. In Helson, H., ed. *Theoretical foundations of psychology.* New York, Van Nostrand, 254-317, 1951.

Brown, J. S. Problems presented by the concept of acquired drives. In *Current theory and research in motivation: a symposium.* Lincoln, Nebr., Univ. Nebr. Press, 1-21, 1953.

Butler, R. A. Acquired drives and the curiosity-investigative motives. In Waters, R. H., Rethlingshafer, D. A. and Caldwell, W. E. *Principles of comparative psychology.* New York, McGraw-Hill, 144-176, 1960.

Cannon, W. B. *Bodily changes in pain, hunger, fear and rage.* 2nd ed. New York, Appleton Century, 1929.

Chambers, R. M. Effects of intravenous rewards on learning and hunger drive. *Amer. Psychol.* 9:346-347, 1954.

Davis, C. M. Self-selection of diets by newly weaned infants. *Amer. J. Dis. Children.* 36:651-679, 1928.

Falk, J. L. The behavioral regulation of water-electrolyte balance. In *Nebraska symp. on motivation* (M. R. Jones, ed.). Lincoln, Nebr., Univ. Nebr. Press, 1-33, 1961.

Freud, S. *New introductory lectures on psychoanalysis.* New York, W. W. Norton, 1933.

Fuller, J. L. and Jacoby, G. A., Jr. Central and sensory control of food intake in genetically obese mice. *Amer. J. Physiol.* 183:279-283, 1955.

Harlow, H. F. The heterosexual affectional system in monkeys. *Amer. Psychol.* 17:1-9, 1962.

Harlow, H. F. Mice, monkeys, men and motives. *Psychol. Rev.* 60:23-32, 1953.

Harris, L. J., Clay, J., Hargreaves, F. J. and Ward, H. Appetite and choice of diet. *Proc. Roy. Soc. Ser. B 113:* 161-190, 1933.

Hebb, D. O. *The organization of behavior.* New York, Wiley, 1949.

Hunt, J. M. Experience and the development of motivation: some reinterpretations. *Child Development.* 31:489-504, 1960.

Irwin, F. W. Motivation. In Helson, H., ed. *Theoretical foundations of psychology*. New York, Van Nostrand, 200-253, 1951.

Keller, F. S. *Learning: reinforcement theory*. Studies in Psychol., New York, Random House, 1954.

Kinsey, A. C., Pomeroy, W. B. and Martin, C. E. *Sexual behavior in the human male*. Philadelphia, W. B. Saunders, 1948.

Kinsey, A. C., Pomeroy, W. B., Martin, C. E. and Gebhard, P. H. *Sexual behavior in the human female*. Philadelphia, W. B. Saunders, 1953.

Leeper, R. W. A motivational theory of emotion to replace emotion as disorganized response. *Psychol. Rev. 55:* 5-21, 1948.

Lehrman, D. S. On the origin of the reproductive behavior cycle in doves. *Trans. N. Y. Acad. Sci., Ser. 2, 21:*682-688, 1959.

Leuba, C. *The sexual nature of man*. Studies in Psychol., New York, Random House, 1954.

Lorenz, K. Z. The comparative method in studying innate behavior patterns. In *Physiology mechanisms in animal behavior*. New York, Academic Press, 1950.

Lorenz, K. Z. *King solomon's ring* (translated from the German). New York, T. Y. Crowell, 1952.

MacLean, P. D. Psychosomatic disease and the visceral brain. *Psychosomatic Med. 11:*338-353, 1950.

Magoun, H. W. Caudel and cephalic influences of the brain stem reticular formation. *Physiol. Rev. 30:*459-474, 1950.

Masserman, J. H. *Behavior and neurosis*. Ch. 5. Univ. of Chicago Press, 1943.

Mayer, J. Regulation of energy intake and the body weight: the glucostatic theory and the lipostatic hypothesis. *Ann. N. Y. Acad. Sci. 63*(1):15-43, 1955.

Miller, N. E. Learnable drives and rewards. In Stevens, S. S., ed. *Handbook of experimental psychology*. New York, Wiley, 1951.

Miller, N. E. Experimental studies of conflict. In Hunt, J. McV., ed. *Personality and the behavior disorders*. New York, Ronald, Vol. 1, 431-465, 1944.

Miller, N. E. and Dollard, J. *Social learning and imitation*. New Haven, Yale, 1941.

Mowrer, O. H. *Learning theory and personality dynamics*. New York, Ronald, 1950.

Myers, A. K. and Miller, N. E. Failure to find a learned drive based on hunger; evidence for learning motivated by exploration. *J. Comp. Physiol. Psychol.* 47:428-436, 1954.

Olds, J. and Milner, P. Positive reinforcement produced by electrical stimulation of septal area and other regions of rat brain. *J. Comp. Physiol. Psychol.* 47:419-427, 1954.

Richter, C. P. Biology of drives. *J. Comp. Physiol. Psychol.* 40:129-134, 1947.

Scott, J. P. and Fredericson, E. The causes of fighting in mice and rats. *Physiol. Zool.* 24:273-309, 1955.

Sheffield, F. B. and Roby, T. B. Reward value of a non-nutritive sweet taste. *J. Comp. Physiol. Psychol.* 43:471-481, 1950.

Stellar, E. The physiology of motivation. *Psychol. Rev.* 61:5-22, 1954.

Tinbergen, N. *The study of instinct.* Oxford, Oxford Univ. Press, 1951.

Warden, C. J. *Animal motivation.* New York, Columbia Univ., 1931.

White, R. Motivation reconsidered: the concept of competence. *Psychol. Rev.* 66:297-333, 1959.

Young, P. T. Motivation of animal behavior. In Stone, C. P., ed. *Comparative psychology.* New York, Prentice-Hall, 1951.

Index

DATE DUE